B␣

AND F␣

by
C. A. House

Read Country Books
Home Farm
44 Evesham Road
Cookhill, Alcester
Warwickshire
B49 5LJ

www.readcountrybooks.com

© Read Books 2005
This book is copyright and may not be
reproduced or copied in any way without
the express permission of the publisher in writing.

ISBN No. 1-905124-56-2

Published by Read Country Books 2005

British Library Cataloguing-in-Publication Data
A catalogue record for this book is available
from the British Library.

Read Country Books
Home Farm
44 Evesham Road
Cookhill, Alcester
Warwickshire
B49 5LJ

BANTAMS
AND HOW TO KEEP THEM

Black-tailed White Japanese Bantam Cock

[Frontispiece

BANTAMS
AND HOW TO KEEP THEM
A Practical Guide to the Housing, Breeding,
Feeding, Showing and General
Management of Bantams

BY
C. A. HOUSE

PRINTED IN GREAT BRITAIN BY
M. F. ROBINSON & CO. LTD., AT THE LIBRARY PRESS LOWESTOFT

CONTENTS

LIST OF PLATES

BANTAMS

AND HOW TO KEEP THEM

CHAPTER I

INTRODUCTORY

THE wonderful growth of the Bantam Fancy during
the last twenty years has been one of the most
striking features of the Poultry world, so vast has
it become that at the Crystal Palace Show the figures
have exceeded 1,500. Apart, though, from those who
keep Bantams for exhibition, there has been a large
increase in the number of people who keep them as pets.
It is true that a few of the old varieties have dropped
out of favour, and some even lost altogether, but their
places have been taken by new varieties, and by an
increased representation of some of the other old-estab-
lished breeds.

Much of the increase in the Bantam Section of the
Fancy is, no doubt, due to the rapid growth of fanciers'
societies in our towns. Many a town dweller of to-day
spent his boyhood in the country amidst poultry and
other live stock, and although the exigencies of space
will not allow of a number of large fowls being kept
in a townsman's backyard, or in the little garden at-
tached to the villa residence of the dweller in suburbia,
yet room can often be found for a pen or two of Bantams.

It is many years ago that I first exhibited Bantams,
and nearly forty that I had my first big win—first
and second at the Dairy Show of 1890. I never at

any time kept a large stock, never more than eight or
nine breeding pens and only occasionally exhibited, my
multifarious duties as a pressman leaving me little time to
indulge in the hobby to any great extent.   Still, no one
is more fond of Bantams than I am, and I hope that
this book will assist in spreading the love for Bantams.
For the town dweller who is fond of poultry a pen or
two of Bantams affords scope for the exercise of the
fancier's spirit.   Many people are deterred from keeping
large poultry by the objections raised by neighbours
to the noise made by the cocks, but few there are who
would object to the music of a pen of Bantams.

EASILY ACCOMMODATED

Wherever space is a consideration, Bantams afford
the delight which is withheld by the inability to keep
larger birds.   It is not only because Bantams require
little space that they are so popular, it is also because
they may be petted and made more fuss over than any
of the larger breeds.   It is this great degree of fami-
liarity which they attain which makes them such great
favourites.   They require little space, eat little food,
give a minimum of trouble, and yet afford a maximum
of pleasure.

A pen of Bantams is easy to manage, and with ordinary care and attention will yield not only pleasure but
profit.   Most of the varieties lay fairly well, and the eggs
are most delicious and dainty, whilst if they are kept
with a view to show, good prices can always be obtained
for first-class birds.   On several occasions Game
Bantams have been sold for £50 each, and many have
changed hands at £20 or £30.   Amongst the other
varieties, Black Rosecombs have repeatedly fetched £20,
and £25 each, and only a little while back one of our
leading breeders disposed of a quartet for £80.   This
being so, it will at once be seen that there is money in
Bantams, and that it is quite easy to combine pleasure
and profit in the keeping of a small stud.

PLENTY OF SCOPE

In the Bantams we have representatives of nearly every breed of large fowl, and they afford plenty of scope for all the skill and ingenuity which any fancier may possess, and so varied are they in form, colour and feather that it is possible for the tastes of all to be provided for. If something fine and racy is desired, then the Game, Old English Game, and Rosecombs will provide it. If delicacy and beauty of marking are needed, then it may be found in the Sebrights, Andalusians, Scots Greys, and the Indian Game. If quaintness is desired, what can supply it better than a pen of Frizzles or one of Japanese ? If it be feathered properties that are admired, then the Brahmas, Pekins, and Booted can satisfy and supply the need in this direction ; and if brilliancy of colour is needed, what can supply it better than the Partridge and Black Wyandottes ? Above and beyond all this, Bantams are very quiet and contented in their disposition and will thrive and do well in places quite unsuitable for the larger breeds. It is this which causes them to be such great favourites with children. They become very tame and docile, and seem capable in the highest degree of appreciating the admiration and attention bestowed upon them by those who attend to their daily wants. By their pertness, by their sociability and by their beauty do Bantams appeal to all who love the denizens of the Poultry world. I shall deal with the subject in a manner which I hope will prove not only interesting to fanciers generally, but instructive to those who have to conduct their breeding operations in the confined space of a suburban garden.

CHAPTER II

HOUSING

THE housing of Bantams is not an expensive matter, because a house 4ft. square, with a run of 16ft. by 4ft. is ample accommodation for a cock and five hens, the number I usually run together. My own houses are of this size, and 4ft. of the run is underneath the house, the floor of each house being raised 2ft. from the ground. This space affords a dry and warm shelter for the birds, and is utilised for the purposes of the dust bath, being kept covered with a mixture of dry earth, ashes and sand. Each run is boarded up 2ft. from the ground, and then is wired with inch mesh wire-netting to a height of 6ft. ; 8ft. of the run proper is covered with corrugated iron, leaving 4ft. to be covered with wire-netting. I have five of these houses and runs fixed in a row, and for a suburban garden I consider this the best type of house and run for the purpose. The roof of the house slopes from front to back, being 4ft. high in front and 3ft. at the back, to which a gutter and spout are fixed to carry away the rain water. At the front and back of each house is an open space twelve inches by four, covered with perforated zinc, and fitted with a sliding shutter for ventilation purposes. These spaces also serve as windows. The perch is fixed in the middle of the house, and the nest boxes, four in number, are at the back. Half of the front is fixed, and the other half is the door ; in the fixed part is the opening by which the birds obtain ingress and egress to the house, and this is fitted with a sliding door which is let down at night during the winter months. The birds reach the house from the ground by means of a short ladder. The floor of each house is covered with finely ground peat moss to the depth of two or three inches. This prevents the house becoming foul, as all the dampness from the excreta is absorbed by the peat moss which acts as an absorbent and deodorant. It also affords the birds much amusement and exercise, as they spend a lot of time scratching about in it and dusting themselves, seeming to prefer it almost to the dry earth outside.

KEEPING THE GROUND SWEET

In these houses and runs I have kept Black Rose-combs, Polish, Old English Game, Modern Game, Malays, Sebrights, Frizzles and Silkies, and find they do well. The ground in the runs is forked over once a week, and this keeps the birds active, as they are continually scratching for worms, etc. I have growing in my present runs two apple trees, a pear tree and a plum tree, and in the summer these afford nice shade for the birds. During the summer months each run in turn is rested and sown down with agricultural mustard seed. This not only keeps the ground sweet, but provides green food for the birds, and thus fulfils a double purpose. These houses and runs are made of inch boards tongued and grooved, the posts and stays being two by two. All the outside woodwork is painted dark green, except the roof, which is covered with asphaltic felt. In the middle of each run is a doorway by which access is gained to the runs, thus on entering the first pen I go from end to end without having to come out and enter each run separately.

I have seen houses fitted on the same principle, but made in a square with runs on either side, that is, two runs in front and two behind. I have also seen them of octagon shape, with the runs going all round, and this, where there is room, is a capital arrangement.

UTILISING THE WALL

Another good type of house, and one which I have used, is a lean-to which may be fitted against the garden wall or fence with the run alongside the fence, the latter forming the back of the run and shielding the birds from the wind. There are a number of houses made by the firms who advertise in the columns of the " POULTRY WORLD," which are admirably adapted for Bantams. One friend of mine who is a breeder of Black Rosecombs, uses as homes for his birds the small houses which are used for the accommodation of the breeding pens at some of our shows. These are fixed at different spots in his garden, the bottoms are covered with loose, dry litter, the nest boxes are placed at the end near the door, the perch runs from end to end, and in bad weather and at nights during the winter the sliding shutter makes all snug and comfortable. Each pen has a run which is half grass and half fine gravel and sand. The one drawback to such houses is that if there are many rats about they obtain easy access to them. The covering at the bottom of such houses needs renewing pretty frequently, or it is apt to emit a nasty musty smell, owing, I suppose, to the dampness arising from the earth.

Nowadays, when such a number of houses varying in design, price, and size are offered ready-made by the firms who make a speciality of such, it is really not worth while for one to build his own. Few, indeed, there are who do so. In my journeying up and down the country I find very few breeders using home-made houses ; even our large breeders find it cheaper and better to purchase ready-made the houses which they require. These houses being made in sections, all carefully and correctly fitted and marked before leaving the works, are very easily put together by anyone capable of using a hammer and driving a screw. Not only are they superior in style and finish to the home-made article, but above all they are cheaper. Most of these firms now send out a combined house, scratching shed, and run. The house is 5ft. long, 3½ft. high and wide. The shelter is the same size, whilst the run is the same width, 10ft. long and 2½ft. high. The cost of the whole thing—house, scratching shed, and run, including a floor for the house—comes out at about three or four guineas. Thus no one need be deterred from keeping

Bantams on the score of the cost of building a house and run.

Those who have the command of a large garden or field, and who are able to let their birds have free range, will have no need of enclosed runs ; all that is needed under such circumstances is a good house and scratching shed.

THE RIGHT SORT OF PERCHES

Perches are an important consideration for Bantams. Those who live in the country, and whose birds delight in a semi-wild or natural existence, will be able to fix up boughs of trees as perches in their houses, and when this can be done there is not much doubt that it is conducive to the bird's comfort. Those of us, however, who are condemned to work out our existence in or near a large town cannot give our birds these luxuries. Unsuitable perches cause the birds uneasiness, and also spoil their carriage. The perches which I use are one and a half inches square, with the rough edge taken off the top ; these drop into slots so as to be easily unshipped for cleaning. I find the birds rest easily and firmly on these, as I have never had a bird go " duck-footed " or bumble-footed.

Nest boxes again are worthy of consideration. Bantams are fussy little individuals with their likes and dislikes, and I think they like a comfortable nest box. My nest boxes are 10 inches square, the back is open, the back of the house acting as the back of the nest box, the top is solid, and across the front three inches up from the bottom runs a piece of wood so as to keep the nests in place. In regard to nest boxes it is as well to have one too many in a house rather than one too few.

Many people whitewash the insides of their Bantam houses. I never do. I keep them thoroughly clean by sweeping down with a short-handled brush, and scraping, should occasion arise, and painting them once or twice a year with creosote. This is a most excellent preservative of the wood, and it has the added advantage of keeping the house sweet and clean, disinfecting it, and at the same time keeping in check all insect life. One word of caution : never put white or light-coloured birds into a house within three weeks of its being creosoted. If you do the colour will be affected.

Many of our large breeders adopt the system of farming out their chickens. They give a cottager two or three sittings of eggs, the cottager finds the broody hen, attends to and feeds the chickens until they are five or six months old, then the breeder comes, looks them over, takes away what he likes at a price previously agreed upon, say 4s. or 5s. each, and leaves the rest with the cottager. The breeder, of course, only takes such birds as are likely to make exhibition birds, or else be valuable for stock purposes. If the hatching season has been a successful one, the cottager is well paid by the money received, and the breeder has some well-grown and choice birds reared away from the main stock without any trouble to himself, and which, having been fed and reared on different food, water, and soil to those hatched at home, keep up the vigour and stamina of the general stock. The wasters, of course, the cottager is allowed to kill or dispose of as he likes.

In the housing of Bantams two things must be avoided. The one is draughts, the other damp. Therefore, see to it if you would have healthy, paying stock, that your houses are draught and damp proof, and that the runs are not allowed to have pools of water standing about them.

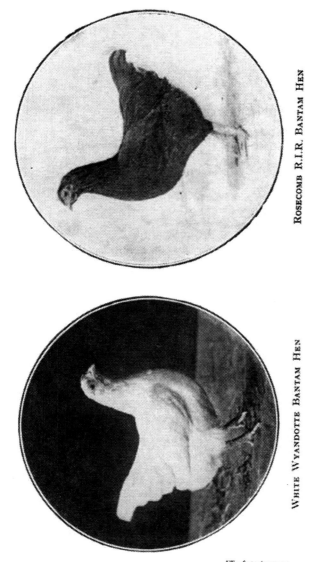

ROSECOMB R.I.R. BANTAM HEN

WHITE WYANDOTTE BANTAM HEN

[To face page 14

WHITE WYANDOTTE BANTAM COCKEREL

ANCONA BANTAM COCK

[To face page 15

CHAPTER III

BREEDING

To all genuine fanciers the breeding season is the most interesting section of the year's work. During its progress there is always something to keep one's energies from flagging. From the time when the foremost breeding pen is put together in the early months of the year, until the chicks have made their initial appearance in the show pen, it is one long round of glorious expectation and pleasurable excitement.

In the mating of birds for stock much care and thought is needed. So many points go to make up an exhibition specimen, and these must all be considered, as must the questions of age, stamina and blood relationships. I must at the outset impress strongly upon the minds of young fanciers the fact that pedigree is to be considered far more than mere outside looks. A flash-looking pen of birds may breed good chickens, but a properly selected pedigree bred pen are certain to do so. When birds are bred to pedigree, or family, there is a concentration of the properties which are required, but when a lot of high-class birds from different strains are put together the result is, in nine cases out of ten, most disappointing, as no matter how carefully each individual bird in the pen has been bred, it has been upon different lines from that of the rest, and the result is a backward step instead of a forward one, the mingling of strange blood producing a strong tendency to reversion, and undoing all the good work that has been done before in building up the originals.

The best plan for a novice to adopt is to go to some well-known breeder, tell him exactly how much money can be spent on a pen of birds, ask him to mate up a quartet, or a quintet, to the value, and leave the rest to his honour and generosity. It is seldom that this plan proves unsuccessful. In purchasing a pen of birds it is advisable to find out all one can as to their family history, so as to be able in future matings to carry on the good work upon the same lines as the original owner. In all breeding operations the great aim is uniformity and concentration. That is, uniformity in the points required, and concentration of them in all subsequent breeding operations. This can only be done by knowing exactly how each bird in one's stud is bred, and then in-breeding, so as to stamp the family characteristics upon the generations yet unborn.

THE BOGEY OF IN-BREEDING

Much that is foolish and injurious has been written upon the question of in-breeding. In-breeding is generally supposed to be the mating together of close relations, but this is not so. True in-breeding means the concentration of all the excellencies of a breed in one particular strain, and so mating the birds that every bird in the stud is more or less related, not necessarily closely related, but having the same blood as every other bird in the stud running through its veins. When this is the case there is some certainty about the results which may be attained in breeding, and unless such a course is pursued success cannot be attained. The one thing to remember is never to breed from an unhealthy specimen. Strong, vigorous birds, possessing the necessary properties, may be bred together as closely as one likes, and no injury will result. In fact, nothing but good. It is impossible to stamp any particular property upon a strain unless one does in-breed, and it is equally necessary to in-breed to keep the points one already has secured.

As to the best time to breed, much depends on circumstances. If one wants very early birds then the stock birds must be mated up in December or January, so as to produce chickens in February and March which shall in the ordinary course of time and with good luck be ready for the early shows ; but if the big events of the year are the ones which are thought of, then April or May-hatched chickens will be early enough to represent the stud at the Dairy and Palace.

The number of hens to be mated to one cock will vary, according to the breed, the time of the year, and the age of the birds. A strong, vigorous early bred cockerel will be capable of attending to more hens than a cock two or three years of age. Again, during the later months of the season a cock or cockerel will fertilise more eggs than he will in the cold, damp days of January or February. Then such breeds as Old English Game, Rosecombs and Indian Game must not be managed on quite the same lines as Sebrights, Pekins and Brahmas. The cocks of the first-named batch are, generally speaking, more vigorous than the latter, and whereas two or three hens will be sufficient for a cock in the latter group, the number may be doubled in the former.

THE QUESTION OF SIZE

As size, or rather, the lack of it, is a most important consideration with the Bantam breeder, it must receive much attention in the breeding operations. Some fanciers like small hens ; others, and they are in the majority, think the cock has the bigger say in this matter, and I agree with them. My experience convinces me that the sire influences size more than the dam. Size in Bantams is a relative quality and quantity. A Bantam is a Bantam, 'tis true, but that does not mean that all Bantams should be of the same size. A Bantam of any breed should bear a relative value to the same breed in large fowls. For instance, a Malay Bantam should be much larger than a Modern Game, an Indian Game Bantam should be larger than an Old English Game Bantam, a Brahma or Pekin Bantam should be larger than a Rosecomb or Sebright, and so on. As affording some guide as to the relative weight of Bantams and the larger breeds, the standard given by the late W. F. Entwisle, the most scientific breeder of Bantams the world has ever known, is, in my opinion, a good one.

B

Mr. Entwisle used to contend that a Bantam should weigh one-fifth of the weight of the larger breed which it typified. Weight and size, however, are not always synonymous, as a soft-fleshed and soft-feathered bird, will look larger than a hard-fleshed, muscular one. As an instance, Polands, Pekins and Frizzles look much larger than they really are, because of the abundance of feather which they carry, whilst, on the other hand, Old English Game and Indians are really larger and heavier than they look.

To get back, however, to our breeding pen, I prefer a small cock or cockerel, with medium-sized hens and pullets to a large or medium-sized cock or cockerel and small hens or pullets. The latter are far more apt to suffer from egg-binding than are their larger sisters, apart from the fact that the bigger the cock or cockerel the bigger the chickens.

NATURAL AND ARTIFICIAL INCUBATION

The question of incubation is one which needs much careful thought. Hens, and hens only, do I recommend for Bantam rearing. My own experience causes me to write thus. An incubator will hatch Bantams all right, but the foster mother is a poor substitute for the hen, and will not answer with the more delicate varieties. Bantam hens of the sitting varieties invariably make most excellent mothers, but as they are so small they are not of great service when one wishes to raise a number of chicks. Thus the question arises, Which hens are the best for a Bantam breeder to use ? Silkie hens or hens of a Silkie-Wyandotte cross make most excellent mothers for Bantams. They are extremely careful and gentle, whilst their long fine feathers afford the chicks warm covering. The one drawback to the use of Silkies, or Silkie bred birds, is their proneness to scaly leg. This, however, can be avoided if care is exercised in the selection of the hens, and attention given to them whilst hatching out and brooding the chicks. Amongst Bantams themselves, Malays, Indian Game, Brahmas,

Pekins, Polish, Wyandottes, Rocks, Frizzles, and Booted Bantams make most excellent mothers, and cover a fair number of eggs, but the smaller breeds are not of much service because half a dozen eggs are as many as they can cover, and eight is the maximum number which should be placed under any of those I have named, especially early in the season ; later the Indian Game, Malays, and Pekins will cover nine or ten ; still, I prefer the smaller number. A Silkie will cover a dozen ordinary Bantam eggs, whilst a Silkie-Wyandotte can manage fourteen or fifteen. Amongst the large breeds I have found Silver Wyandottes and Buff Orpingtons the most reliable, most careful, and most satisfactory mothers for Bantam chicks.

WHERE TO HATCH

The broody hens should be set away from the Bantam runs if at all possible, as the presence of the other birds is apt to disturb and unsettle the broodies. An orange box fixed up in the corner of a shed or outhouse makes a good sitting box for a trio of hens. The bottom of each division should be filled with fine earth or a turf of grass, which should be moulded into a bowl-shaped form and then lined with some nice short, soft, well-rubbed hay or straw. The reason for having the hay or straw in short lengths is that there is less likelihood of it getting wound round the legs of the broodies, and so the chances of the eggs being pulled out of the nest are minimised. In setting hens it is advisable to do so at night, and let them have twenty-four hours on dummy eggs before you place in the nests the eggs which are to be incubated. This allows them to settle down and avoids the breakage of many a good egg.

Five or six days from the time of the eggs being set they should be tested. This is best done at night, when by holding the eggs one by one between the forefinger and thumb, in front of a lamp or candle, you can easily tell if they are good or not. If they are fertile you will see little red veins running like railway lines in all directions ; those unfertile will be clear. These should be removed, and only those allowed to remain which are fertile. In the early part of the season it may happen that quite half of the eggs will, when tested, be found unfertile. In such circumstances, if two hens have been set at the same time, one may be given all the fertile eggs, and the other given a fresh batch. This is a saving of time, trouble and expense, in addition to which a hen always seems to do better with a fairly large family than she does with a very small one.

If the weather is very dry during the period of incubation, it is the custom of some breeders to sprinkle the eggs every day during the last week, whilst others give them five minutes' soaking in warm water on the eighteenth day, that is the day before they are due to hatch.

HOW TO TREAT THE BROODY

When selecting a broody hen look well to her legs, see that they are clean. Never select a hen with scaly leg, for if you do, of a surety you will have scaly legged chicks, and once a clean-legged Bantam has suffered from scaly leg much of its value as an exhibition specimen is gone, because smart, clean legs add greatly to a bird's appearance. The feather-legged birds suffer much from scaly leg, but even with them it is not advisable to court trouble by using broodies with scaly legs. When she is placed on the eggs she should have a small quantity of insect powder well rubbed into the feathers, under her wings, on the back and cushion, and about the root of the tail. The nest itself should also be well dusted with the powder. Each morning or evening, whichever suits best, the hen should be lifted off her nest, given a drink of water, and a feed of maize or wheat. She should also have the chance of a dust bath, and the picking of some grit. Whilst she is off the nest, the eggs may be examined to see if any have been chipped or broken ; if so, they should be removed, and any which may be soiled should be washed in warm water, and then returned to the nest. Should it happen that the nest itself is soiled, the hay or straw should be removed and a fresh supply given. The hen should be examined to see if any broken egg is adhering to her feathers ; if so, she should be given a good sponging with warm water all over the breast and under parts of her body, but care must be taken to dry her with a soft towel before she is allowed to go back to the eggs, or the wet, sodden feathers may be the means of another smash. Whilst the hen is sitting I always keep a sack in front of the box, this keeps everything quiet and secluded.

On the nineteenth day, counting from the day when the eggs were given to the hen, the chicks may be expected. If the hen is quiet and sensible I think it is best to leave her alone, only looking at the nest about every two hours to clear away the empty shells. If this is not done they are apt to cover the eggs which are not yet chipped, and prevent the chicks from getting out. Should it happen, however, that the hen is fussy and restless and likely to trample the chicks, it is wise to take them away as hatched and place them in a box near the kitchen fire, first lining the box with a piece of old flannel, leaving enough lap on the flannel to cover the chicks. They will dry off nicely in this box and when all are hatched they may be returned to the hen at night, and the chances are that by morning she will have settled down, and everything will proceed favourably. If an old shed can be utilised, it is wise to leave the hen and her family in the same for a few days before transferring them to a coop on the grass. Bantams are at all times most susceptible to the evil influences of damp, but particularly so during the first few weeks of their life. Therefore if they can be kept snug and dry in a shed for a few days until they are well on their legs, they will thrive all the better when they get outside.

CHAPTER IV

REARING

FOR the first twenty-four hours after hatching the chicks will not require feeding, nature having provided for their sustenance and nourishment in the shape of the egg sac, which is drawn up into the body at the time of hatching. Many fanciers feed their young chickens on hard-boiled eggs and bread crumbs, using both the yolk and the white ; some use the yolk of the eggs only ; others use a custard made of eggs and milk ; others, again, use from the first feed one of the advertised prepared chicken meals, whilst some feed on dry food only. I have never, for newly-hatched chicks, used either egg and bread crumbs, or custard, and once only did I try the dry food system. The result was not satisfactory, for all the chicks died. It may not have been the dry feeding, or it may have been. My system of feeding is that which was followed by that very successful Yorkshire breeder and well-known judge of the days that are gone—the late Enoch Hutton.

HOW IT IS DONE

I boil rice in water, cooking it thoroughly, and letting the rice absorb all the water. When putting the rice in the saucepan, I add a pinch of salt and a piece of suet about the size of a walnut to each small teacupful of rice. When cold, I feed this to the chicks, first mixing with the rice a little finely ground oatmeal. This I feed from the first meal right on till the chicks are a fortnight old, varying it now and then with rice pudding made with milk. At the end of a fortnight I give one meal a day of dry chick feed, and at the end of the fourth week the dry chick feed is given twice a day. This I have found a good nourishing diet, and one upon which the chicks feather well. Occasionally, even if reared on grass, the chicks may be given a few lettuce leaves, dandelion leaves, or spring onion tops, but all of these should be cut up fine before giving. They will be much relished by the chicks and do much good in cleansing and cooling the blood.

THE OTHER WAY

Those who advocate the use of egg and bread crumbs proceed on the following lines. They first give very finely chopped hard-boiled egg mixed with double its weight of bread crumbs, or they mix the egg and bread crumbs together and then press them through a sieve, or one of the patent potato-squeezers, such as cooks use. This feeding is given for the first five or six days, after that a little boiled rice is mixed with it, gradually increasing the rice, and when the chicks are a month old they are placed upon a diet in which one of the prepared chicken foods is the principal factor, whilst when the chicks are about a fortnight old they are given broken wheat, canary and other small bird seeds twice a day between the feeding of the soft food.

Which ever system of feeding is adopted, it must ever be remembered that the one royal road to success in chicken raising is feeding little and often whilst the chicks are growing and feathering. Thus for the first fortnight they should be fed every two hours, from then till they are a month old every three hours ; after that four times a day will suffice until the sexes are separated, and from then onwards three times a day will be sufficient.

CHANGE OF FOOD

When the chickens have got nicely feathered—say, about five or six weeks old—they will need to be put upon a different food régime, according to the breed. Those that are short of leg and very feathery will need plenty of rice, which, although it does not produce bone, does influence feather considerably, not altogether because of its own nutritive qualities, so much as it does by its action in keeping the blood cool, and thus allowing the other foods given to be assimilated with ease and comfort without the skin becoming dry and irritated, and thus acting as a deterrent upon feather growth. If stimulative and nourishing foods only are given, the blood becomes over-heated, and the skin is apt to become dry and harsh, and when this is the case the feather does not break nicely. This is a big drawback when one wants to grow a lot of feather, and grow it quickly, too. In the harder-feathered, longer-legged, and more muscular breeds one does not need to give so much rice, but rather more wheat.

When they arrive at this age, the short-legged, heavily-feathered birds should be given two feeds of the soft food and two of dry chick feed twice a day, whilst the harder feathered birds may be given soft food only in the morning, the other three feeds being one of the prepared dry chick feeds, or a mixture of groats, broken wheat, dari, millet, canary, and other small bird seeds. Water should be given regularly from the start of the dry feeding, but care must be taken to keep it shielded from the sun, as sun-warmed water is very apt to cause diarrhoea. Whilst chicks are being fed upon soft food only, or even when they have one feed a day of dry chick feed, I never give water.

NEED OF EXERCISE

Chickens should be given plenty of exercise if they are to keep healthy and strong, whilst the hard-feathered breeds, such as Game, Malays, and Indians, want a wide range. To keep chickens healthy they should be made to scratch well for all their hard food, and this they will do if it is scattered amongst the grass or litter. I make a practice of always placing some soft food in the coop the last thing at night, so that the chicks may have a feed the first thing in the morning. Some fanciers give their chicks a feed of bread and milk, or some such dainty, by candle-light. This I have never done. It seems to me to be opposed entirely to nature. Chickens, like all other growing animals, require a certain amount of rest and sleep. If their slumbers are disturbed they do not get it, whilst another objection I have against this night feeding is that it puts too great a strain on the digestive organs. A chicken derives nourishment, not from the quantity of food which it consumes, but from that which it assimilates. If the food is not properly digested, it passes away without fulfilling its functions, and the chick, instead of being nourished, is starved, as, owing to the over-taxing of the digestive organs, they are unable to extract nutriment from the food given. The digestive apparatus of a chicken requires rest just as much as the other organs. A system of cram may be all right for a bird that is required for the table at an early date, but for a chick which has to keep healthy and grow feather, as an exhibition Bantam has to do, it is all wrong.

THE WEANING TIME

The chicks may run with their mother until they reach the age of ten or twelve weeks, if she does not tire of them. Hens differ very much in this respect. I have had hens that would brood the chicks until they were almost full-grown, and lay an egg every day as well, whilst others, commencing to lay when the chicks were six weeks old, would at once show that the days of maternity were over, and that the hitherto fond mother no longer desired her chicks, and, by pecks from her beak and blows from her wings, began to make them understand that they must keep at a distance. At whatever age the chicks are separated from their mother, they may run together until they are about sixteen weeks old. It is then advisable to separate the sexes. At times it is needful to do it even earlier than this, owing to one or two precocious cockerels wanting to boss their brothers and sisters. Bantam chicks should not be allowed to perch before they are four months old,

say many writers, or they will be crooked-breasted.
I am inclined to think that this is one of those rules
which, being accepted as gospel truth, has been handed
down from generation to generation without being tested.
I have had chicks perch from the age of eight weeks, and
never had any evil results therefrom, but, then, my
perches are broad enough for the birds to secure a good
foothold.

The sexes having been separated, we may consider
the rearing season practically at an end, and therefore
I close this chapter, leaving the after career of our
future winners to be dealt with under other headings.

CHAPTER V

GENERAL MANAGEMENT

THE sexes having been separated, we may take it that
our birds are chicks no longer, and must now be given
the treatment which is to continue for the rest of their
life. At the time of separation all that are not worth
keeping from a breeding point of view, or that are not
likely to grow on into exhibition specimens should be
killed. It is useless keeping a lot of birds about which
will never be fit for the show or breeding pen. They
interfere with the growth of the other birds, preventing
their development of feather and style, fouling the
ground, increasing the tendency to disease, and adding
very materially to the corn bill. Thin them out ruth-
lessly. Birds that show glaring faults of colour, feather,
shape, comb, or lobe, should be given the happy despatch, and all that may show any symptoms of being
sickly and weakly.

THE VALUE OF SHADE

Whilst the birds are growing and feathering they
should be shaded. All Bantams need shelter, whether
old or young, not only from sun, but from wind and rain.
If it is at all possible to secure it there is nothing to equal
the shade of a shrubbery or coppice, but such shade is,
of course, not available to the town dweller or the sub-
urbanite. Where it is not possible to secure the shade of
trees and shrubs much may be done by the erection of
canvas screens, the use of closely woven hurdles, or by
open sheep hurdles covered with sacking. Two such
hurdles fixed into the ground with their tops meeting in
apex fashion, and with a third placed at one end make
a most desirable shelter for growing chicks in a large
run, and if a liberal supply of scratching material is
placed under the hurdles the chicks will keep under

27

them whenever the sun is strong or the wind rough. Any fancier with a fair amount of ingenuity will be equal to devising shelter for his birds according to their necessities. It must ever be remembered that all birds of white, buff or other delicate colours must be shielded from sun and rain all the time they are growing their adult feathers ; if not, such birds as the whites, piles, birchens, and duck-wings will be tanned and the buffs will be faded. All birds which are intended for exhibition, no matter what their colour may be, should be shaded from the direct rays of the sun during the hours when it is high in the heavens, as it has a tendency to destroy the bright, glossy appearance of the feather.

GENERAL FEEDING

Bantams must be well fed, but not over-fed. In other words their food should be of the best, but they should not be fed to repletion. When they have left the days of chickenhood behind them my birds have a warm feed each morning ; sometimes it is one of the prepared biscuit meals, at others it is a mixture of sharps, stale bread and house scraps, about one handful of either to each trio of birds ; at mid-day they are given green food, and at night a feed of corn ; a handful is sufficient for each trio, the latter is generally wheat, varied at times by rice, dari, canary seed, or dry chick feed. Where a larger stud is kept this feeding can hardly be followed, and in such cases a larger range in meals may be used. Some writers recommend oats as one of the grains for Bantams, but my birds never seem to care for them, and I may say the same of buckwheat. Maize also is a grain I never use for Bantams. One thing should never be forgotten, and that is that all grain fed to Bantams at one time should be that of one kind of corn only. There is no change of diet when mixed corn is used. During very cold weather I sometimes give my birds a little hemp seed in the middle of the day, and I find they appreciate it greatly. It warms and stimulates them, and given judiciously acts advantageously on their generative and reproductive organs.

GREEN FOODS

Birds that are kept in confined runs must be liberally supplied with green food. During the spring and summer months grass cuttings from the lawn, lettuce, cabbage, onion tops, broccoli leaves, dandelion, groundsel, and other garden refuse are all useful, and all much appreciated by the birds. In the winter months when green food is scarce and difficult to obtain, swedes, mangolds, and beetroot are good substitutes. A little chopped onion is also relished. Where birds have free range over grass it is not necessary to provide them with any other kind of green food or roots, yet if such are given the birds will relish them. With them as with their owners, " variety is the spice of life."

THE WATER SUPPLY

The water supply deserves far more consideration than many breeders give it. Those who live in the country and have plenty of range for their birds with running streams or a good pond which is supplied from a stream or spring, need never trouble about supplying their pets with water, but those not so happily situated must remember that water is one of the things Bantams cannot do without. Water, and pure water, they must have, and if it is not supplied to them fresh every day, and in nice clean vessels, their health is sure to suffer.

I always use earthenware vessels for water myself. Earthenware pots and fountains are more liable to breakage than metal ones, but they are much to be preferred from the sanitary aspect. Earthenware is easily cleansed, and it has this advantage over metal, that if it is needful to give the birds medicine through the medium of drinking water, no evil results follow. In the winter time earthenware vessels must be emptied each night, or the frost might burst them.

In the summer time care should be taken to stand the drinking vessels in the shade. Sun-warmed water is apt to cause diarrhoea. The drinking vessels should be thoroughly cleansed daily. Many fanciers just empty the stale water away, give the fountain or pot a rinse round, and put in the fresh water. This is not enough ; the vessels should be well rubbed round with the hand so that the sediment is cleansed right out. Whilst the chicks are growing it is a good plan to put a few crystals of permanganate of potash in the drinking water every other day. This acts as a tonic and blood purifier, and tends to keep away roup and other affections of the throat. Another good tonic which may be given occasionally is sulphate of iron, a piece about the size of a hazel nut is enough for a quart of water.

GRIT AND ITS USES

It is most essential that Bantams should have a supply of grit. Birds which are kept short of grit never do well. Some fanciers supply it in a grit box, others mix a handful with the soft food every other day. It is immaterial how it is given, so long as it is given. Birds which are given grit regularly keep in better health and lay more eggs than those who are not so catered for. I use a mixture of cut flint and crushed oyster shells, not the mixture which is sold for poultry, but that which is known as Pigeon size.

CONSIDERING THE BREED

When one contemplates the vast extent of the Bantam family it quickly becomes apparent that with such widely divergent characteristics in the different breeds the management must also of necessity be totally different. For instance, feather-legged breeds, such as Pekins and Booted, need different housing to Game and Malays. High-class specimens of the feather-legged varieties do better if they are not allowed to perch during the time their feathers are growing, and during the exhibition season, as in flying up and down to their perches they are apt to break their leg-feather. Again, they must not be allowed to run loose over rough ground, or through long wet grass, as such is ruinous to the production of feather. Further, the feeding of long-feathered birds needs to be entirely different to that of the hard-feathered. The long-feathered birds need feeding with more soft food than the hard-feathered. As a general principle free range and hard feeding tend to shortness and hardness of feather, whilst soft feeding and restricted liberty are conducive to long and soft feather. Thus all hard-feathered birds should be given free range and made to work for their food.

NOT WISE TO FORCE

It is not wise to force Bantams, as when stimulating foods are used the birds are apt to become large and coarse in body, and that is a thing which we want to avoid. No matter what the breed, size has to be kept down, therefore meat must not enter, to any extent, into the dietary. Those who breed for feather will find in bread and milk, and rice boiled in milk, quite sufficient stimulus for the needed feather. Rice is a good coat grower. The only time when I force my birds at all is in the early part of the breeding season, when the weather is cold and damp. I then give a little meat in the morning meal, and now and again a handful of hemp at mid-day. This is done to counteract the deadening influence of the east wind, and to put a little extra fire into the birds' systems.

CHAPTER VI

EXHIBITING

HAVING decided to test the merit of his birds at some show, the owner should catch his selected bird, or birds, and place it or them in pens, and for this purpose it is wise to fix up a range of show pens in a shed or outhouse ; if such is not available, the conservatory may be used, but if no outside accommodation is available, and often it is not with the small breeder, the owner need not be deterred. He should utilise the kitchen table at night time, when it is not required for other purposes. One thing is certain, and that is, that some sort of training is needful before birds are shown, and he who would succeed must adapt himself to the circumstances in which he finds himself placed. When and where it is possible, the birds should be given a week or ten days in the pens previous to a show, so that they may become thoroughly accustomed to them, learn to stand well, and show off their points to perfection.

TAMING AND TRAINING

When birds are placed in the pens they should be fed carefully with the object of their plumage presenting the best possible appearance by the day of the show, and the first step in that direction is to give them for a few days, say, three or four, a pinch of Epsom Salts each morning, as much as will cover a sixpenny bit heaped up. This is done with the object of cleansing the blood. The morning feed should be meal, mixed with a little boiled linseed, or, if preferred, a handful of crushed linseed may be mixed with six handfuls of the ordinary meal. If whole linseed is used it should be boiled and used with the jelly. A teacupful of linseed should be placed in a quart of water, and allowed to simmer on the hob until it is a thick jelly. This would be sufficient to mix with the meal for a score of birds. The meals used may be any of the advertised biscuit meals dried off with sharps, or a mixture of sharps and barley meal in equal proportions, and a sixth part each of pea meal and fine bran. Not much of this should be given, only about half the quantity the birds would have when at liberty ; at midday a little rice and canary seed may be given ; these are both good conditioners, and at night hard grain, wheat for preference, should be fed. Green food in some form or other should be given daily. A little bread and milk may be given late in the evening ; it is a good conditioner. Grit and water must also be provided, and some sulphate of iron should be given in the latter three times a week, a piece about as large as a horse-bean to a tea-cupful of water.

Each time the birds are approached they should be spoken to, and tempted to come to the front of the pen by the inducement of a few grains of hempseed or small pieces of raw meat. With such birds as Modern Game and Malay, in which reach is a consideration, the tit-bit offered should be held as near the top of the pen front as possible. The object of this is to induce the birds to come to the front of the pen when the judge approaches them in the show. Being used to receiving dainties at home they look for them abroad. After a few days, and when the birds have become accustomed to the pen, the judging stick may be introduced. This should be done very quietly and carefully at first. I have seen young cockerels plunge and fly about like mad when they first caught sight of a judging stick. When such happens combs get damaged and sickles broken and this is most certainly not desirable. Therefore, introduce the judging stick cautiously. If the bird is at all nervous, speak quietly and soothingly to it, gain its confidence, let it understand there is no need for fear. If the bird is at all wild withdraw the stick, open the pen, and take the bird out, hold it in one hand whilst you stroke it down with the other. Do this for a few moments, then return it to the pen, and pass the hand over its back a few times. When you have succeeded in getting it to stand steady have another try with the judging stick. Pass it gently over the bird's back from the head to the tail a few times, and then leave it. The next day have another try, and you will find nine times out of ten the bird will have overcome its fear of the stick. Then proceed to lift its tail, touch the under portion of its body, and generally habituate the bird to the use of the judging stick. If a bird is inclined to carry its tail high stroke it down repeatedly with the judging stick, so as to induce a lower carriage of the tail.

Should it happen that a bird has a low carriage of wings or tail, the same can be much improved by lifting the flights or tail, as the case may be, with the judging stick each time you put the bird through its paces. The continued lifting of the wings or tail teaches the bird what is needed. If the wrong carriage is the result of some structural defect or malformation, the training will not correct it, but more often than not such things are the result of habit. There are lazy, slovenly birds, even as there are lazy, slovenly men. Bad carriage of body may also be considerably improved by touching the bird underneath its body, and by rapping its legs with the stick. It is wonderful what effect a few lessons in deportment have upon birds. At the close of each lesson the bird may be given a few grains of hemp or canary seed. If the lesson is given at night the feed of bread and milk mentioned earlier in this chapter may be give at its close. Get the bird to connect the training lesson with something pleasant, and your task will be considerably lessened.

TRAINING FOR THE SHOW PEN

Birds that have had free range usually take the most training, whilst those reared in small runs are so used to close contact with their owner that they have no fear of him. Further, such birds naturally get more handling during the time they are growing up than do the others. A well-trained bird of average merit will often beat a superior ill-trained one. When a judge has from 400 to 500 birds to get through in a morning he cannot waste time trying to get bad showers into position, and the bird that responds to his call readily and smartly will beat the one that is wild and restless, or the one that is slow and awkward.

Many a prize is lost owing to the wildness, nervousness, or slovenliness of birds, therefore the time spent in training a good bird and familiarising it with the show pen is sure to bring rich reward. A bird that is tame and well-trained seems to enjoy being shown, and to delight in showing off its excellencies before an admiring crowd. Such a bird is at all times a source of pleasure and pride to its owner, and in addition, some profit, because it invariably catches the eye of the judge.

Dark plumaged birds require little preparation for show. A rub down with a damp sponge, followed by a soft cloth and then a silk pocket-handkerchief, is all that the plumage needs. Wash the comb, lobes, wattles, legs and feet in warm water, with a sponge and a little soap ; dry carefully with a soft cloth, and then rub the comb, wattles, and legs over with an oiled rag just before you put the birds in the basket to despatch for the show. White and light plumaged birds will require washing.

BEFORE THE SHOW

Before birds are despatched to a show they should have a good feed, something that will stand by them. It is not at all unusual for birds to leave home early in the morning to arrive at the show the same night or first thing the following morning, and as birds are seldom fed at shows until after judging it means that those which have come from a long distance have to go about thirty hours without food. For this reason do, I say, give a good feed of wheat before the birds are packed. Soft food does not stand by the birds long ; it is quickly digested, and its nutritive value readily assimilated by the bird's system ; thus for birds fed on soft food before their departure for a show there is a long fast.

In sending birds away to shows see to it that the baskets are sound and in good order, no broken wicker, no holes in the lining, and all fastenings sound and secure. Many a good bird has been injured by reason of the lining of the basket being torn, and affording the bird the opportunity to get its head outside, to say nothing of the chance it gives inquisitive railway servants and others to interfere with the birds, whilst many a bird has escaped owing to insecure fastenings. Therefore, see that all buckles and straps are in good working order a few days before the birds have to be despatched. Don't leave it to the last moment, and then have to patch up a damaged basket or strap.

AFTER THE SHOW

When the birds return from a show they should be unpacked at once and given a little warm soft food, a meal mash with a sprinkling of cayenne pepper is as good as anything. After they have fed give them a drink of warm milk, in which you have mixed a few drops of gin, say, ten drops of gin to a wineglassful of milk. It often happens that after a show birds suffer from congestion of the liver owing to the extremes of temperature met with at the show, and on the journey to and fro. For this reason do I advocate the above treatment.

The soft food is easily digested, and thus, after a long fast the bird is re-invigorated more quickly than if fed with hard food. The cayenne pepper is stimulating and warming, acting directly on the liver, whilst the milk is soothing and thirst quenching ; and the gin, like the cayenne pepper, is stimulating and warming, whilst it also acts directly upon the kidneys. Thus, by the aid of two simple agents—cayenne and gin—any congestion or tendency thereto is corrected quickly and thoroughly.

It is wise to keep all show birds penned up by themselves for a few days after their return from an exhibition, in case they may have been in contact with birds suffering from any contagious disease. Not long since a fancier, and a very prominent one, too, lost about £500 worth of stock through one of his birds bringing diphtheric roup back from a show.

The risks of showing are great ; therefore, it is advisable to put a few grains of permanganate of potash in the drinking water given to birds for a few days after their return from a show. Should by any chance the birds have been near any birds suffering from roup, this simple, yet effective, corrective may save the life of the champion of one's stud.

CHAPTER VII

WASHING

THE task of washing a Bantam is sufficient to frighten many a good fancier, and no power on earth could persuade them to make the attempt. To anyone who lives in a town where the atmosphere is laden with soot, the knowledge of how to wash is one of the first conditions of a successful career. The man who lives in a town, and yet can manage to show white or light plumaged Bantams, and win, deserves all he gets, if only for the trouble entailed in washing his pets and preparing them for the judicial eyes. I have won many a prize by condition and cleanliness of feather, and I have sometimes lost through want of it. Over and over again I have envied some of my colleagues who are situated in a district where smuts, soot and smoke do not abound.

The art of washing is not at all an easy one, and very few fanciers there are who can be styled expert laundrymen. If a bird has to be washed, it wants to be done well, or else not at all ; a badly washed bird looks worse than one on which no attempt has been made. To start with, I may as well say that no one should ever wash a Bantam unless obliged to do so.

Washing certainly puts on a very spick-and-span appearance for a time, but it does the bird no good constitutionally, neither does it improve the feather permanently, but quite the reverse. When a bird has been washed two or three times, the feather loses its nature and becomes harsh and dry looking, whilst every time a bird is washed it soils more quickly after. The most suitable time for washing is in the evening, after tea, when the little ones are gone to bed and the house is nice and quiet. Further, it is better for the birds to be washed after they have had their evening meal than when they have no food at all inside them.

THE FIRST ATTEMPT

The washing process is often a stumbling block to young fanciers. I well remember with what feelings I approached " my first." More can be learnt from one practical illustration than by reading a number of treatises on the subject. Those who are acquainted with a skilled exhibitor should, if possible, gain admission to his sanctum when he is putting some of his gems through the refining process. The operation of washing a Bantam is, to the novice, a most difficult undertaking, and should he be at all nervous, it is liable to end in a disastrous manner. Two things are necessary to the operator, namely, a fair share of nerve, and plenty of confidence in his own ability to bring the operation to a successful issue.

Before commencing operations on his show specimens the operator should practise with a few common birds, for if the attempt should end in the maiming, laming or killing either of these specimens, the loss will not be great. If successful with these commoners, this will give sufficient confidence to put more valuable specimens through the process. After a short time the necessary confidence and knack of handling the birds will have been acquired, and the washing of five or six birds will not cause more uneasiness than will be felt in performing the same operation on one's own self.

PREPARING THE FIRE

An important consideration is the fire, this should be bright, yet not too fierce. In making it up it should be well stirred with the poker, and all dust removed. The best way to make up a fire for drying birds is to use equal quantities of coal and coke ; nice knobby pieces, about the size of a teacup should be used. A fire made in this way will throw out a steadier heat than one made with coal only ; it will also produce less smoke. Whilst the fire is burning up, the few articles required to successfully accomplish the task should be collected together. These are three good-sized bowls, two small honeycomb sponges, a tablet of soap, two or three nice soft cloths (discarded chamber towels will do very well indeed), a jug for cold water, a jug for hot water, a tin of borax, a bottle of glycerine, and the household bluebag.

As to what soap is best, opinions differ. One thing must be guarded against, and that is common soap. The best soaps are more free from alkali than the common ones, and thus by their use the colour of the bird's plumage is not injured. The effect of using common soap is that the alkali contained in it draws the colour from birds of delicate plumage. In addition to the articles I have named, a drying cage of some sort is required. Some fanciers use a large box with a wired front. I, myself, use a large poultry basket, which is covered three parts of the way round with canvas. The bottom must be covered with chaff or some such substance. This will soak up any excrement that may be avoided, and thus prevent the birds from soiling their plumage whilst in the drying box, or cage. The two cloths that are to be used for absorbing the moisture in the feathers of the birds should be hung on the drying cage or basket in front of the fire ; this will warm them and prevent any draught getting at the birds whilst they are drying.

All things being in readiness, some cold water should be placed in each of the basins, and slightly tinged with washing blue ; then add sufficient hot water so that you can comfortably bear your hand in it. If the water is hard a very small piece of washing soda should be added to that placed in the first basin ; this will soften and assist in removing the dirt more freely. Don't put too much. A piece about the size of a hazel nut will be ample.

Take your soap and with the sponge work up a good lather in the first basin. A little glycerine should also be placed in the rinsing water, about a teaspoonful to a quart of water. In each of of the rinsing waters place a teaspoonful of borax which has previously been dissolved in boiling water. The rinsing waters should also be just tinged with blue if you are washing white or very light plumaged birds. The blue is not needed with coloured birds, and with such the soda and borax should also be left out, as they are strong alkalies and have a prejudicial effect upon the colour.

You will now be quite ready to commence operations. First of all, take the bird you intend to operate upon in your hands, with its head towards you. Immerse it in the lather for a moment or two previous to using the sponge. The object of this immersion is to let the water saturate and soften the feathers, so that when you begin to rub them with the sponge they will not break. It is a good plan to gently move the wings and tail to and fro in the suds. The motion has a tendency to withdraw the dirt from the feathers, and saves rubbing. Don't rub the feathers more than you are obliged. Being ready to start the rubbing process, commence by spreading the right wing over the fingers ; give it a good soaping with the sponge, then turn the bird round in your hand and serve the left wing in the same manner ; next place the bird on its back, and apply the sponge to the under parts of the wings, tail, and body. Attention should now be given to the head and neck, and it is here that most care will be required. The dirt seems to cling more firmly to the head feathers than it does to any other part of the body. Great care is needed in keeping the soap out of the eyes. A little soap will not hurt, but should too much be used the eyes may sustain serious injury. It is a good plan to soften the dirt round the head by rubbing with the finger, and then the sponge need only be used very little near the eyes. If the wings and tail are very dirty they should be spread out on the table and rubbed well with the sponge.

HOW TO CLEAR THE SOAP

Having completed the lathering process, you should now proceed to get the soap out of the feathers. Hold the bird securely in the hands, and give it a good rinsing in the second basin, then finally rinse it in the third basin. Don't be afraid to use plenty of water, give the bird a thorough sousing, for unless you get every particle of soap out of the feathers your labour will be thrown away. Should any soap be left in the feathers the bird will present a very rough appearance when dry. The rinsing being finished, draw the wings and tail smartly through the hands—this will extract much of the water ; then mop the body with the second sponge. Then take one of the cloths, roll the bird in it, and wipe your hands on one of the others. Having done this, throw one end of the cloth over your left hand, place the bird in it with your fingers and thumb under its wings ; take the other end of the cloth in the right hand and proceed to dry the back, wings, and tail, at the same time so manipulating the left hand that all the water in the under part of the body may be drawn out. Then straighten the wings and tail with the right hand. The whole of the drying operation should be performed as near the fire as possible.

NEVER BE NERVOUS

Some birds stand the washing much better than others, and it takes little effect on them, but on some of their weaker brethren it has a very exhausting effect. If a bird should look as though it is approaching its end when laid in the drying hamper you need not be alarmed ; after lying like that for some little time it will get on its legs and pull itself together. Fatal results from washing birds are few and far between. When they do occur, it is generally by the bird being held too tightly. Some birds struggle very much whilst being washed, and should you feel at any time that a bird is going to elude your grasp, it is best to let it go, you can easily pick it up again, but should you make an effort to tighten your hold on it, you will be almost certain to harm it. If the bird is held firmly in the way I have described, it will not be able to struggle much. If you are at all nervous, your grasp of the bird will not be firm. By some intuitive instinct birds always seem able to tell if the person handling them is nervous, and they act accordingly. But when secured in a good, firm grasp, they, as a rule, struggle little. There is a great art in handling birds, an adept at the practice feels as much at home when handling one of his little pets as a mother does when fondling her infant child. The birds know and appreciate the difference between the two systems.

DON'T DRY TOO QUICKLY

The birds should not be allowed to get too dry in the drying cage. When about half dry, they should be taken out and allowed to flap their wings a bit, this assists in the webbing of the feathers. The birds must be held tightly by the thighs during this process. In an hour they should be moved to the other side of the room. It takes ten or twelve minutes to wash a bird, and it should be in the drying cage fifty or sixty minutes. Don't dry them too quickly, or the feathers will be hard and harsh. All pens in which newly washed birds are placed should be scrupulously clean, or washing will have been labour in vain. Birds with soiled plumage stand very little chance on the show bench nowadays ; competition is so very keen that the slightest difference in condition oftentimes turns the scale.

In the opinion of some fanciers, Whites and such birds as Piles, Columbian Wyandottes, Light Sussex and Light Brahmas, are the only varieties which are improved by washing. This is a mistake, some of the coloured varieties are much improved by a wash.

CHAPTER VIII

GAME BANTAMS

By time-honoured usage, the pride of place is given to Game Bantams, and yet they are not the oldest, being of more recent introduction than such breeds as Rosecombs, Nankins, Sebrights, Booted, and others ; still, in most popular works on Bantams, and in the schedules of our shows, premier place is given to the Bantams called Game, the reason, doubtless, being that they are more largely bred than any other variety. For many, many years this could have been said of the Modern Game Bantam alone, but of late the Game family have only been kept in the topmost place by the advent of the Old English Game Bantam, which to-day is without doubt the most widely known, and most largely bred of any of the Bantams. As showing how very modern is the Old English Game Bantam, I need only remark that in the monumental work on Bantams, written by England's greatest Bantam breeder and authority, the late W. F. Entwisle, published in 1892, the Old English Game is not given a place, and only incidentally mentioned in a passing reference.

IN BYGONE DAYS

It is now about sixty or seventy years ago that the Modern Game Bantam was first introduced to the English Fancy by the late John Crosland, of Wakefield, a most ardent lover of the Game Fowl, and one whom it was my pleasure to number amongst my acquaintances. Mr. Crosland and Mr. Entwisle were near neighbours and close friends, and if the one introduced the Game Bantam, the other did much to perfect it. Considerably altered in general appearance is the present-day Game Bantam from what I remember it in my youth. My impression is that the variety then exhibited was neither the present Old English nor yet the present Modern, but there is no doubt to which side it inclined, and that side was not the Old English. In general, the same qualifications we sought years ago are sought to-day in the Modern.

GENERAL CHARACTERISTICS

The chief points in all classes of Game Bantams are shape, style, colour, feather (hard, narrow, short, and tight fitting), and smallness of size. Taking shape first, the bird should have a long lean head, a fine, graceful, well-curved neck, the shoulders should be broad and square, and carried rather prominently, the chest proportionately broad, but not too prominent ; the body should be short (a long body being a great fault), and taper well off towards the stern—" well cut away " is the term oft used in describing it ; the back should be flat, the thighs long and muscular and set well apart, the shanks fine and round, the toes should be long, and straight, the hind toe being set opposite to the middle toe. This is most important, as it gives the bird the proper grip of the ground, which is needful for it to show itself properly. Some birds have this back toe set on too high, and then only the tip touches the ground, at other times, the toe is too low, it grows inwards, or sideways, and causes the bird to be " duck-footed." This is a disqualification. As this hind toe plays such an important part in the show pen, breeders should exercise the greatest care in their selection of breeding stock, as bad feet are often inherited. The sides of the body should be well rounded, the wings short and clipped in close to the sides ; if carried too high it is a fault, and such is styled " goose-winged." The tail should be small and fine, very compact in formation, and carried slightly above the body. The tail proper should contain fourteen feathers, and the sickles or side feathers should be very narrow and fine and neatly curved, but they must not droop, neither must they be forked. The eyes in Black-reds, Piles, Duck-wings, and Whites should be bright red ; in Brown-reds and Birchens the darker the eye the more valuable it is. The Game Bantam when in the show pen should be tall, erect, and reachy, presenting a general appearance of smartness and alertness.

Size is an important point, but one which is often carried to extremes. The craze for smallness has rendered some strains almost worthless, the hens being generally very delicate, and often quite unfit to breed from ; indeed, many of them die in the attempt to lay their first egg. One point in connection with size which needs remembering is feather. A coarse-feathered bird looks larger than it really is, whilst one that is hard and neat in feather looks smaller than it is. Again, a tall, reachy bird may often be larger and heavier than a shorter-limbed bird, but it does not look it, owing to the fact that its height takes off the appearance of heaviness. Some people talk a lot about the weight a Bantam should be but the really practical fancier rarely gives weight a thought—he goes by the appearance. Still, as a direction and assistance to young fanciers who may not be able to gauge their birds by the eye, and who may possibly like to have something to guide them, I may say that a cockerel should weigh from sixteen to twenty ounces, and a pullet fifteen to eighteen ounces ; adult birds will weigh from two to four ounces more. These are normal weights for birds living in a natural state, and fit to breed with. When put into pens, and fed, prepared, and trained for the show bench with their flesh and muscle hardened, they would weigh two or three ounces less.

CHAPTER IX

BREEDING GAME BANTAMS

BLACK-REDS

HAVING given the general characteristics—i.e., the points which all Game Bantams have in common, I now come to speak of those which pertain to each individual colour, and pride of place naturally falls to the Black-reds. Colour is a great point in all Game Bantams, and the breeder who would scale the highest point of the Fancy must give much thought to its production. The face, wattles, throat, lobes, and head of a Black-red cock should be bright-red, the neck hackle bright orange red, the back and wing bow rich bright crimson, the saddle hackle should match that of the neck. The wings should have the butts black, with bars of steel blue, the flights or wing ends should be a clear rich bay or chestnut, the breast and thighs should be a rich deep blue-black, perfectly free from ticking or any sign of rustiness, the tail and sickles should be black, including the shaft, the beak, legs, and the feet rich olive or willow, and not showing any tinge of blue.

The exhibition Black-red pullet should in eyes, beak, legs, feet, head, wattles, comb, and lobes resemble the cockerel. The neck hackle should be a light gold, with well defined, but very narrow, black stripes down each side of the shaft, with a clear golden edge all round the black. The back, wings, and outer feathers of the tail should be one uniform shade of a light, soft, brownish drab, each feather being finely and evenly pencilled with black ; coarse pencilling is very objectionable ; red or rusty feathers in the wing are also a great fault in the exhibition pullet. The tail, with the exception of the outer feathers mentioned, should be black. The throat should be a pale salmon colour, shading into a rich deep salmon as the breast is reached, and then shading off again towards the thighs and under parts of the body.

BREEDING

These are the colours required in the exhibition cockerel and pullet, but two such birds mated together will
not breed exhibition birds of both sexes. They would be
all right for the production of show cockerels, but not
for pullets, and even for cockerel breeding they may be
improved upon. In breeding their exhibition cockerels
most breeders use what are known as Wheaten hens or
pullets. These are paler in colour than the exhibition
pullet, being lighter on breast, less striped in hackle,
and show foxy or wheaten coloured feathering on the
wings. Such birds, however, will only breed show
cockerels ; for breeding exhibition pullets they are
worthless. The great value of the Wheaten in breeding
exhibition cockerels is that the top colour is brighter
and clearer than when Black-red exhibition pullets are
used.

In the breeding of pullets the chief consideration is
the soundness of colour in the hens or pullets which are
used. They must be quite free from rust or coarseness
of pencilling. The nearer they approach to the exhibition standard the better. The cock or cockerel used in a
pullet breeding pen should not be an exhibition bird, but
one bred from a pullet breeding strain, and darker in
colour than the show bird. In top colour he should be of
a brickish-red from neck to tail, his wing bars and
shoulders should be quite free from lacing, and as black
as possible. Good pullet breeding cockerels are usually
light in the shaft of their tail feathers, and also their
wing ends.

Those who have limited accommodation may breed
both exhibition cockerels and pullets from one pen,
but the results are not so certain, neither is the percentage of high-class birds so great as when double mating is
followed. Those who can only manage one pen should
select a cockerel from off a pullet breeding strain, one
similar to the bird described as a pullet breeder, but a bit
lighter in top colour if possible. Such a bird should
have as his mates good sound coloured exhibition pullets

Modern Game Birchen Bantam Pullet

Black-Red O.E. Game Bantam Cock

[To face page 48

Partridge Yokohama Bantam Hen

Pile Game Bantam Cock

[To face page 49

or hens. Never on any account use Wheaten hens in
your single pen, because if you do you will not keep
either your body or leg colour sound.

BROWN-REDS

In colour the Brown-red has not such variety as the
more gorgeously apparelled and popular Black-red,
being quieter and more sombre in its plumage. The
face, comb, and wattles of the cockerel should be black ;
the beak the blackest horn colour ; neck, saddle, and
wing bars should be bright clear lemon yellow ; the rest
of the body should be rich glossy green black ; the
feathers of the throat and breast should be laced with
lemon, the lacing to commence at the top of the throat
and be continued down to the thighs ; the tail should be
black, and as fine and as short as possible. The Brown-
red pullet should correspond with the cockerel in beak,
face, eye, comb, wattles, legs and feet. The head feathers
and neck hackle should be lemon striped with black ;
the rest of body in rich glossy green black, with the breast
lacing extending, as in the cockerel, from the throat
to the thighs. The feather all over the body must
be solid in colour and show no lacing or paleness of
shaft.

HOW TO PRODUCE

To breed Brown-reds for exhibition it is almost imperative to resort to double mating, especially for cockerels, in breeding for which one must secure as head of
the pen the most perfectly coloured cock or cockerel to
be found ; he should be well laced on the breast, but
clear on the wing butts. The hens or pullets for such
a bird should have lemon-coloured heads and be as pale
in neck hackle as possible. Dark capped hens or pullets
are of little use in the production of exhibition cockerels.
If, however, they are laced on the back, so much the
better, your cockerels will come with purer and clearer
top colour. The pullets bred from such a pen would be

D

useless except as breeders, but as such they would be invaluable.

When one is breeding for pullets it is necessary that the hens or pullets in the pen should be of exhibition form, or as near to it as can be obtained, whilst their mate should be a bird that is too dark in colour of hackle and top for exhibition, but he must be sound in eye, and very clear and regular in his breast lacing. From such a pen as this the pullets should be near to exhibition form, whilst the cockerels would be too dark, but would have much value as pullet breeders.

PILES

Next to the Black-red the Pile is undoubtedly the most popular, even as it is the most handsome. Substitute white colouration for the black of the Black-red cockerel, and you have the Pile cockerel; that is, the breast, thighs, wing butts, wing bars, and tail should be white, with rich orange yellow beak and legs; the face, wattles, comb, and lobes should be rich bright red. The eyes of Piles should be red, and as rich in colour as possible. The hackles should be rich clear orange yellow in colour; the back, saddle and wing bow should be rich bright red of a sound even shade. The most difficult point to obtain is the pure white breast, many otherwise good birds showing signs of ticking, or cloudiness of colour.

The exhibition Pile pullet should have the same coloured beak, eyes, face, comb, wattles, lobes, legs, and feet as the cockerel. The neck hackle should be golden yellow with a narrow white stripe down each feather; the breast should be a pale salmon with the colour shading off as it approaches the thighs, the body, wings and tail should be a white—the standard says pure white, but such is seldom, if ever, seen; the colour most generally met with being a creamy white. It is very difficult in breeding pullets to obtain rich breast colour, and at the same time a clear wing, many good pullets showing a bit of colour in the wing.

MATING FOR SHOW BIRDS

In Pile breeding, as with the Black-reds, two pens are needed for the production of exhibition stock, and colour is one of the most important points. Therefore, in selecting a pen to breed cockerels, it is most essential that the head of it should approach near to the exhibition standard for cocks. His mates should be deep in breast colour, and show some colour in the wing ; they should be what is known as " rose-winged," also show some colour on back, and have richer coloured hackles than exhibition pullets.

For breeding exhibition Pile pullets our hens or pullets must be near to the standard in all points. The cock for such birds should be sound on his wing ends, clear on his shoulders and wing bars, and if laced somewhat on the breast it is a recommendation. Much depends on strain and how the birds are bred, and in purchasing stock one should get to know as much as they possibly can of the past history of the birds. This is most important, because nearly all breeders use Black-red blood amongst their Piles, and if this gets into the hands of a new beginner who knows nothing of the system which governs the use of such blood it will ruin his stud right from the start.

OUT-CROSSING IN PILES

In breeding Piles there is a tendency for the colour to become paler after a few seasons' breeding of Piles to Piles, and to restore it resource is had to the Black-red blood. If the failing colour is on the cockerel side, then a Black-red cockerel must be used to restore it. Such a cross will also tighten and harden the feather. The bird to be selected should be short and fine in his feather, very rich in top colour and saddle, and deep dense black on breast and wing bars, with rich chestnut wing ends. The last point mentioned must never be overlooked. In using a Black-red cock to improve the colour in your Piles, you must mate him with very pale coloured hens or pullets, such as are known as lemon Piles—that is, birds with very little breast colour. The cockerels resulting from such a cross will have yellow legs, but the majority, if not all, of the pullets will have the willow legs of the Black-red. The latter, however, are generally purer in their white and deeper in their breast colour than the yellow legged pullets, and if carefully mated to a cock from an established pullet-breeding strain they will produce most excellently coloured pullets.

If the out-crossing into the Black-reds is done with the intention of improving the colour of a pullet strain of Piles, a yellow legged Black-red cockerel, one bred from Piles, may be used. Another way of improving the colour in a Pile pullet strain is to mate a pale coloured Pile cock with Black-red pullets from a pullet strain, whilst a cross between a Pile cock and Wheaten hens is of great assistance in improving a strain of cockerel-breeding Piles. Piles were first produced by the crossing of Black-reds and Whites, hence the reason why the Black-red blood is so valuable to the Pile breeder in maintaining his colour.

To the small breeder, the man who only has a few birds, I would say leave the crossing into Black-reds alone, or you may spoil yourself a whole season. The better way in a small yard is to secure an extra good coloured cockerel from a cockerel or pullet strain, as may be required, trusting to the infusion of new blood to replenish your own strain.

DUCKWINGS

Duckwings, like Piles, take a lot of breeding, the colour difficulties at times being such as to try the patience and enthusiasm of the most ardent. In colour the Duckwing cockerel is a very smart fellow, with his rich red face, lobes and wattles, clear red eye, silvery white head feathering and neck hackle, rich orange back and wing bow, silvery white saddle hackle, black breast, belly, thighs, wing butts and bars, white wing end, black tail, and willow legs and feet.

The Duckwing pullet should match her mate in face, eye, comb, wattles, and lobes, legs and feet, her breast must be salmon coloured like unto that of the Black-red pullet, shading off to ashy grey on the thighs and belly ; her body colour must be a French grey or pale slate, and must be very finely and regularly pencilled with black ; her head feathering and neck hackle must be white striped with back ; the tail black with the top outer feather marked like the back and wings.

In breeding Duckwings few there are who breed from Duckwings only, yet it can be and is done, but the difficulty is to keep up the colour, therefore most breeders have resort to Black-red blood, which is done by using a Black-red cock or cockerel to Duckwing hens ; the Black-red must be up to exhibition form. The cockerels only from such a cross would be of use as exhibition birds ; in fact, the pullets would in appearance be Black-reds, but mated to a Duckwing cock they will produce Duckwing cockerels and pullets, being especially useful when raised with cockerels of a cockerel-breeding strain. In the same way some breed from a Duckwing cock and Wheaten pullets, using those that are extra light in colour about the head and hackle. The whole process of breeding Duckwings is very complicated, and there is much difficulty in keeping the colour up to exhibition form unless an occasional dip is made into the Black-red.

BIRCHENS

As I have said, the Birchen is the silver counterpart of the Brown-red, and there is no member of the Modern Game Bantam which has made such rapid strides in popular favour of late years. This doubtless is due in great measure to the fact that it is not so necessary to resort to double mating as it is with some of the other

colours. Still, double mating produces the greater
number of good birds, and most breeders use two pens,
or in other words, have cockerel and pullet strains.
Birchens were first obtained by crossing a Silver Duckwing cock with Brown-red pullets, but so established
have they become that there is no longer any necessity
for the use of alien blood.   Substitute silver for gold
in the Brown-reds and you have your Birchen.   This
being so, there is no need for me to further describe
Birchens.   The chief difficulties in breeding are in keeping the lacing pure in colour and sound, and keeping
the eye dark.   Watch these points carefully and you
will succeed as a breeder of Birchens.

WHITES AND BLACKS

White Game Bantams have been more frequently seen
of late years than they used to be, but they are not likely
to become so popular as their darker brethren, because
they soil so quickly, and are therefore only suitable for
a fancier whose lot is cast in the country.   They are not
a bird for a townsman.   The White Game Bantam
should have a red face, comb, wattle, lobes, and eye, the
beak, legs, and feet should be yellow, the whole of the
plumage pure clear white.   This being so, style and
shape play the greatest part in their breeding.   Blacks
are seldom seen, yet they are very handsome.   The
points are the same as the Whites, excepting the plumage, which should be a deep glossy green black.

CHAPTER X

OLD ENGLISH GAME

THE Old English Game Bantams are practically a 20th century production. It was in the show season 1898-1899 that the boom, so to speak began, and since then they have made most rapid headway. At the time mentioned they were little thought of, and of little worth, to-day they are universally admired, are bred in thousands from one end of the kingdom to the other, high-class specimens fetch most remunerative prices, and there is a strong demand for ordinary stock birds.

A good Old English Game Bantam should be broad in the chest, low on the leg, straight and firm in breast, short in the back, stout in head and beak, possess a clear, fiery eye of a bold, fearless expression ; the legs should be ivory-white in colour and round in shape, fairly stout, and firmly set in the body ; the feet also should be white, and set well on the ground, giving the bird an alert, graceful, yet bold, appearance and carriage ; the wings should be short, meeting under the tail, fitting closely to the body, and should be full, so as to avoid the appearance of flat-sidedness. The tail should be full in feather, with the sickles and side hangers of the cock long, well curved, and gracefully carried. In colour the face, comb, lobes and wattles should be bright red, the plumage hard, firm, and tight fitting.

Old English Bantams are very hardy, easy to rear, lay fairly well—in fact, better than many Bantams—the hens make good mothers, and will look well after a brood of chickens if given the chance. This, together with their tameness and sociability, has no doubt tended to make them very popular amongst fanciers who have only limited accommodation, and like the birds they keep to rear their own young.

55

To a fancier with an eye for beauty there are few breeds to compare with the Old English Game Bantams. Their beautiful plumage and graceful carriage is a sight that invariably attracts the eye of an artistic person. I believe there are more varieties in the Old English Game than in any other breed of poultry. Among the principal colours are :—Spangles, Black-breasted red cocks to be mated to Partridge hens ; Bright-red or Ginger cocks to be mated to Clay or Wheaten hens ; Brown-breasted reds ; Blue-breasted red cocks to be mated to Blue or Blue-wheaten hens ; Blacks ; Blues ; Whites ; Duckwings ; Piles ; Furness ; Birchens ; and Creles. In addition there are Hennies, Tassels and Muffs in some of the colours. The only colour which is at all difficult to breed true are the pure Black cocks, so many of them coming with red or white feathers. Some have the red feathers in the wings only, these are called Brassy wings, and are very handsome, but some come with the red and white distributed here and there about the body.

THE POPULAR SPANGLES

First and foremost come the Spangles ; go where you will nowadays to a show, you are almost certain to come across some Old English Spangle Bantams ; even at shows where only one Bantam class is provided, you will find the Spangles ; they may be said to be ubiquitous. Here, there, and everywhere are the Spangles to be found.

Why the Spangle should have obtained this predominance I cannot say ; probably it is due to its pleasing variety of colour, and the fact that only one breeding pen is required by the lover of the colour. In colour the cock and hen resemble each other in every respect, the plumage throughout being black and red, or blue and red, evenly spangled with white, with the tail black and white and blue and white. The chief and prevailing fault in Spangles of to-day is a tendency to lightness of colour, and this failing is more prevalent in Scotland than in England ; many of the birds across the Border, to use the term of one of our most successful Cumberland breeders, are mere meal bags. Now a light coloured, heavily spangled bird is not nearly so handsome as one darker in colour, and has not so much spangle. What is required is such a complete blending of the three colours that a bird does not look too dark or too light, but presents a beautiful harmonious whole with neither of the three colours obtruding itself too much upon the eye of the beholder. As I have said, the prevailing fault is lightness of colour, but it is one easily remedied. All that is needed is a season's breeding with a Partridge hen, and then the careful use of the pullets bred from her.

BREEDING FROM ONE PEN

When one is compelled to breed from one pen it is wise to select birds that are of medium colour and evenly spangled, birds that are dark in colour or too heavily spangled do not make the best of breeders from an exhibition point of view. They are each inclined to perpetuate their deficiencies. On the other hand a sparsely spangled cock is a good mate for pullets that are inclined to be too heavily spangled, or carry too much white in wings and tail. One thing must never be done, and that is to mate a cock or cockerel that is gaily spangled to hens or pullets possessing the same failing. To do so would be to intensify the tendency to lightness, and make the progeny what I have heard them styled, " regular meal bags." Occasionally a Black-red cock may be mated to spangle hens or pullets to overcome this tendency to mealiness. Another fault, which is rather prevalent in some strains of Spangles and other colours as well, is " white in lobe." In exhibition cocks it is not seen because the birds have been dubbed, and the ear-lobe removed, but it can be seen in the hens. It is a fault that is somewhat difficult to eradicate, but it is one that should be stamped out whenever it makes its appearance, because it is a great drawback to a bird, and there is no comparison between a bird with a rich red lobe and one which shows " white in lobe."

OTHER COLOURS

Black-reds resemble in colour their namesakes in the Modern Game Bantams, and in breeding them both Wheaten and Partridge hens may be used, but it should be said that the brightest and best coloured birds are, generally speaking, bred from Partridge hens, and in Old English Game Bantams a deeper tone of colour seems to find favour with the judges than in the Moderns. Whilst this is the fashion double mating will not be the necessity that it is with the Moderns. One thing must be guarded against if only one pen is kept, and that is the breeding from a Wheaten bred cock ; to keep the colour right only Partridge bred cocks or cockerels must be used. If one has the convenience and the time to attend to double mating then the same lines may be followed in breeding Old English Black-reds as are followed in breeding the Modern Game Bantams.

Blue-reds are not very numerous, although during the past few years the colour is one that has received more attention, and recently a number of breeders have turned their attention to the breeding of the Blue-red. In mating up a pen to produce exhibition Blue-reds, a Blue-red cock or cockerel should be mated to Blue or Blue Wheaten pullets or hens. A mating of Black-red cock and Blue Wheaten or Blue pullets will also produce them. Duckwings, Birchens, and Brown-reds should be bred upon the lines advocated for breeding the Modern birds of those colours, and so far as colour points are concerned the description is the same as for the Moderns. The Creles are very handsome with their Cuckoo marking. They vary much in their ground colour and also in the colour of the marking, some being very dark, almost Black or Blue-reds, with only a suspicion of marking, and that most strongly developed on the breast, whilst others show the Cuckoo marking more or less all over the body, and so strongly that they are almost devoid of any ground colour owing to the happy blending of the Cuckoo colouring.

THE INTRICACIES OF BREEDING

Piles can be bred by mating a Black-breasted Red or a Ginger cock to a white hen, and, although the majority of the first cross may come pure white, if the White pullets are mated to a Black-breasted Red or Ginger cock the result from this second crossing will be Piles, although it is possible some of the pullets may be Clays or Wheatens, and some of the cockerels (or stags, as they are called by the old school of breeders) Gingers.

In breeding it is necessary to breed birds as true to colour as possible ; but in awarding prizes a competent judge will lay more stress on the handling, shape, and carriage of a bird than the markings, colour of eyes, and colour of legs. Light or daw eyes are by some judges considered a disqualification, whilst others are indifferent as to the colour of a bird's eye, if the game properties are good, but I admit that a large prominent red eye is a great set-off to any bird. Among the Black-breasted Reds, Piles, Wheatens, and Whites will be found birds with bright red eyes, while others have light or almost white eyes ; the latter are termed daw-eyed, on account of the colour closely resembling the eyes of a Jackdaw.

In more recent years self Blacks and Blues have become great favourites, and many of the most typical of Old English Bantams are found in these colours. Purity of colour is a great feature in these, but type and feather must never be sacrificed for colour

CHAPTER XI

ROSECOMBS

BEFORE saying anything about breeding, I will en-
deavour to describe an ideal cock and hen. Taking the
cock first, and commencing with the comb, this should
fit very close to the head, be broad and full in front—
" solid-fronted "—taper away gradually to the back,
and finish off with a fine, long leader with an upward
tendency. The body of the comb must be full and
level, evenly serrated and full of work, and like the wattle
and lobes, of a rich cherry-red colour. Head short and
fairly broad, beak stout and short, dark in colour, and
curved ; eyes dark and full. The lobes should be ivory
white in colour, large in size, round in shape, possess
plenty of substance, and be smooth and kid-like in
texture. The neck should be short and stout, covered
with a long flowing hackle, which should come well
down over the shoulders. The back should be short and
broad. The wings large, not too long, and carried in
drooping fashion below the body. The tail should be
large and broad, width of feather both in the tail proper
and in the hangers and sickles being a most valuable
property ; the sickles should be long and gracefully-
curved. The breast broad and full, and carried well
forward. Legs short and fine, black in colour, with
white toe-nails. Carriage, jaunty and lively. Colour
lustrous black, sound and rich, and carrying plenty of
beetle green sheen. Weight 14 to 18 ozs.

Hen.—The comb, head, beak, face, wattles, eyes,
lobes, wings, legs, and feet agree with those of the cock.
The comb, lobes, and wattles are naturally somewhat
smaller. The body is smaller, but the carriage, like
that of the cock, should be alert, lively and jaunty.

THE FAULTS CONSIDERED

Having described the perfect exhibition birds, I will now deal with some of the faults possessed by Rose-combs.

There is only one ideal comb, which all breeders strive for, viz., full fronted, wedge-shaped, tapering off to a fine leader, and full of small risen points, termed work. Many birds there are with shelly combs, which is about the worst comb both for showing and breeding, and one I would hesitate to use in the breeding pen. It is thin and shell shaped in front, hence its name. Then we have the short, stumpy comb and short leader ; another faulty comb is one with a thinness in front, termed "leafy in front," but many a nice comb and full of work I have seen among the latter ; lastly, we get the plain comb ; while such will never do on a bird for exhibition, yet I would never scruple in using an otherwise good bird in the breeding-pen, simply because he was plain in comb. Most of these faults can be bred out with time and care. White in face is a fault, largely due to mating birds possessing too large lobes on both sides. We have also the dark coloured face, which we term gipsy face, which is a fault in a show bird. This fault generally pertains to hens, cockerels scarcely ever being subject to it. This is a fault in the show hen, yet we see plenty of good hens shown that are touched with it. Some strains of cock-bred hens have it, and where that is so, have no fear about the cockerels bred from them, as they will come all right in that respect. Some birds, hens more particularly, are too hairy in face. Strive to breed them with as clear faces as possible.

Colour of eye is most important, a good dark eye is needed ; a red or gravel eye never looks so well as a dark one. If you place two birds equal in head points side by side in a show pen, the darkest-eyed one will appear to have the largest lobe, and will catch the eye first.

More faults, I think, will be found in the lobes than all the rest of the points put together. A cockerel or pullet without some pretensions to a good lobe will never do

for the show bench. The faults of a lobe are numerous.
I will mention a few. A folded or badly creased lobe,
although it may be of good quality, is of no use in the
show pen. If, however, one has patience he can do a
lot towards improving it, and licking it into the desired
shape by gentle massage with the forefinger and thumb
two or three times a day. A blushed lobe, or even one
with a lot of red on the edge, and surface, may be improved by penning the bird indoors, and bathing with
cold water every day, and putting on a paste of Fuller's
earth each night. Another system of treatment followed
by some fanciers is to take a few drops of quintessence
of lemon in a tablespoonful of water, bathe the lobe
and finish off with glycerine and cucumber. Hollow or
folded lobes the amateur cannot do anything for. The
lobes of birds intended for exhibition must be large,
thick, round, and free from any scooping at the top to
mar the complete circle, and must be a lily white colour,
very smooth, and free from creases.

The lobes of a Black cockerel are somewhat of an
anxiety as a bird gets near the adult state. They may
leave the face on the lower side, which is bad ; and if the
bird has been very liberally fed during chickenhood with
a view to get it along as fast and as well as possible,
when full growth has been reached the rich food seems
to have the effect of causing the lobes to blister up. I
have seen beautiful birds for the time being quite spoiled
in this way. They have been forced so as to be ready
for the early shows, and the result of the stimulating
food is seen in the fact that the lobes do not last, and
the exhibition career of such birds is not a long one.

Rich foods, if given during chickenhood to promote
early maturity, must be cautiously used as the adult
stage is reached, and once a bird's lobes are fully up, the
sooner he gets on to plain, natural food, the better ;
otherwise, his blood is thrown out of order, and he
accumulates a watery substance in the lobes, which
comes out in the shape of blisters, and greatly disfigures
the bird. There is nothing for it but to stop off the rich
food at once, bathe the blisters gently in warm water,

and when they burst, dry them as much as possible with violet powder, or finely-sifted starch ; also place the bird in a darkish place in confinement, so that it may run off a bit in condition, and get its blood cooled down. A sulphur and lard pill at such times cannot do any harm. In many cases, if the bird be properly treated, there will be little or no scar visible after all has healed. Prevention, however, is better than cure, and it is far better to miss a few early shows than to spoil what, if left alone, would possibly prove the best bird of the season.

THE VALUE OF COLOUR

Colour is a valuable property in a Rosecomb. The colour of both male and female should be a rich greenish black, with as much lustre as possible. But don't run away with the opinion that lustre is colour, for it is not so. Lustre glosses over many a bad-coloured feather. If there had been more latitude allowed in the size of Rosecombs, I am sure by this time they would have held their own with the generality of Black Hamburghs. The great difficulty lies in getting a good sound colour in conjunction with small size. The day of sooty hackles and dull body colour is past. They are no good in either the exhibition or the breeding pen ; shun them as you would a plague.

Rosecombs should be short in back, but you cannot get the same sweep of the saddle right on to the tail in the short-backed birds as you can on the medium. These short-backed birds are generally the worst defaulters in split saddle. If you can breed them short in back, and also get the saddle or cushion without any split, so much the better. I would here say a few words on the feather of exhibition cockerels. My experience tells me that the tail is not as hard to get as head points ; yet a good tail takes some breeding. It is not so very easy to obtain ; it has to be bred for, and fed for, too. I like to see a fine broad green sickle, with broad green lustrous side hangers properly balanced and carried at an angle of

50 degrees. I also like to see the saddle take a clean, straight sweep on to the tail, and detest a saddle splitting and shedding to each side at the junction of the tail, making it look as if the tail did not belong to the saddle. The standard gives the same for tail points as comb and lobe, but in judging few judges consider tail of the same value as the head properties.

HOW TO PRODUCE WINNERS

In breeding Rosecombs it is not necessary to use two pens, yet our most successful breeders do so because they can breed a larger percentage of show birds by so doing. I will first of all deal with single mating. Those who have limited accommodation must of necessity be satisfied with a single pen. The cock or cockerel selected to head this should be a good exhibition bird with plenty of feather and rich colour. His mates may be two exhibition hens or pullets, and two others smaller in lobe, and possibly not so rich in colour, or the whole four birds may be as near to exhibition form as possible. The breeder who uses one pen only should select a rich green black cockerel, one with beautiful head properties, fine, clear cut, well furnished comb, long strong leader running out straight with the rest of the comb, and not twisted, nor curved, neither turned either up or down. See that he has a sound face, a round, thick, fine-textured, close-fitting lobe, without crease, fold, or stain, and of good size. Look for a full-feathered, shapely bird of graceful carriage, with grand flow of feather, and mate him to hens or pullets that excel in all these points, whether they be show birds or not. If you find that he produces too rich colour, and his chickens come with red feathers about them, then next year mate him to duller coloured females. It is only in this way that you can hope to succeed if you breed from one pen only. It should not be forgotten, however, that the double mating system yields the higher percentage of winners.

BLACK ROSECOMB BANTAM COCK

SILVER SPANGLED HAMBURGH BANTAM PULLET

[To face page 64

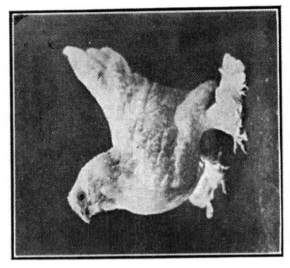

PORCELAIN BELGIAN BOOTED BANTAM HEN

LIGHT BRAHMA BANTAM

[To face page 65

THE COCKEREL BREEDING PEN

A cockerel breeding pen should be headed by a good exhibition cockerel. Such a bird should have for his mates four or five small feathery hens, with good, long, well-marked combs, and nice length of leader. They should be sisters of a good exhibition cock of the same strain, being bred from a cockerel breeding pen, and should possess a good round lobe of nice substance, colour, and texture ; the lobe will often be smaller than that of an exhibition pullet, but this, if the cockerel has good, big, round lobes, does not matter, the progeny will come all right in that respect. These cockerel bred hens have no use in the exhibition pen, owing to their being too small in lobe for present-day requirements, but as breeders of cockerels they are indispensable.

THE PULLET PEN

We now come to the pullet breeding pen. The cock or cockerel to head this pen must have as good a comb as possible, the lobe must be round, and of good quality and colour. He need not, if pullet bred, have a large lobe, but the colour and quality must be there. Let him be a good coloured bird, the richer the better, and if he has a few red feathers in his neck hackle, shoulder, or saddle hackle, he will be all the more valuable as a pullet breeder. All Black strains of good colour throw cockerels of this description. The mates of such a bird should be first-class show hens, or as near thereto as can be obtained, and should be bred from a pullet breeding strain. Let them be as perfect in comb and lobe as it is possible. They should be small, short in body, stylish in carriage. Their faces should be a nice bright cherry-red colour ; gipsy faced hens must never be used for pullet breeding ; they should also be clearer in face, but, above all, they should have a big well-laid-on lobe, one standing well away from the face with a good solid top. Remember, the more substance you can get into the lobe

E

at the top the more likelihood is there of the progeny having lobes that are well laid on. It is the thin lobes which curl, fold, and crease, therefore do I urge so strongly that substance should not be overlooked in making up the breeding pen.

WHITES

White Rosecombs seem to make little headway, owing, no doubt, to the difficulty in keeping them in good plumage. From early chickenhood—that is, as soon as they begin to throw their chicken feathers—they must be kept out of the sun, and from exposure to the weather, or the beautiful colour of their plumage will be spoilt, and instead of being white they will be creamy in appearance. The points of the Whites are the same as the Blacks, but they have one advantage over the Blacks, one pen only is needed for breeding cockerels and pullets. In mating, the great consideration is purity of colour, especially of legs. Birds that fail in leg colour generally reproduce the failing in their progeny, and the leg colour also influences the body colour. Whites have a beauty all their own, and a well shown White Rosecomb with its snow white plumage shows up well against the rich cherry-red of its face, comb and wattles.

THOUGHTS ON SHOWING

To show a Rosecomb properly, a fair amount of time is needed. For a fortnight or so before the show the bird should be penned up and trained in the manner detailed in the chapter on exhibiting. During the time the birds are in the pen, the comb, wattles, and lobes should be washed with soap and water, and dried carefully with a soft cloth. After each washing the lobes should be massaged between the finger and thumb, and then just touched with a little violet powder. At the same time the feathers may be given a nice gentle rub down with a silk handkerchief ; it will do much to improve the gloss and sheen. During the show season birds must be kept in covered runs if they are to be exhibited, because exposure not only roughens the lobe, but dries it up, and also causes it to go red. A blushed lobe, however, will, with the treatment above given, and the confinement of the bird in a semi-dark pen, soon recover its original colour and beauty. A wash occasionally improves the appearance of a Black Rosecomb. As the birds approach the end of the moult their tails and flights should be examined, as some are inclined to be quill bound. In such cases the tail or wing may be sponged for a few minutes with warm water, and then held in front of a fire ; this will cause the sheath to burst, and the feather is not so liable to be damaged as if other means are adopted. The comb also will need attention. The leader may be lengthened and given an upward tendency by being worked between the finger and thumb each day ; inequalities at the front of the comb may also be reduced by carefully kneading it with the fingers. All this is legitimate, but cutting and stitching, of which we sometimes hear in connection with the comb and lobes, is faking, and cannot be too severely condemned. The great thing to do is to strive to breed perfect birds, not make them.

CHAPTER XII

SEBRIGHTS

THERE can be no doubt whatever that the Sebright is one of the most charmingly beautiful of the many varieties of Bantams which we possess, even as it is one of the oldest. We are indebted to Sir John Sebright for this lovely variety. This gentleman, who was M.P. for Herts, was an enthusiastic lover of poultry in the early days of the 19th century.

In olden times the Sebrights had chiefly ruddy faces, combs, and wattles instead of the dark, gipsy, purply tint of the present generation. Again, the eyes were a little more coloury then than now, and, further, in the old sort, the tails were occasionally very much speckled, and the wing coverts rather sooty, smeary, and, further still, the cocks' tails were often a bit curved and spangly.

In the breeding of Sebrights double mating is not absolutely necessary, as both sexes may be bred from one pen both in Golds and Silvers, yet the most successful breeders use two pens, as they say the results are more sure so far as the production of exhibition birds are concerned. If double mating is followed, the cock or cockerel used for breeding cockerels should be clearly, but rather heavily laced, his breast and tail lacing should be very clear and distinct, as should that of his wing ends. In ground colour he should be as clear as possible, and his face should show the much desired mulberry tint ; cocks do not show this over much, still, the darker they are in face the better. His mates should be very finely laced, but yet very distinct, pure black and white in colour, and not showing any inclination to bronze or rust on the margin of their feathers. Their faces should be dark mulberry ; this is imperative. The pullet breeding pen should be mated on opposite lines ; the cockerel or cock should be finely laced, and the hens or pullets more heavily or densely laced, especially on the thighs, tail, and tail coverts, but in each case look well to the tail, wing, and throat lacing ; soundness on these parts is a great consideration. If only one pen is used the cock should be a good exhibition bird, and his mates should be mixed, some light in lacing, and some dark or heavy. By this means you will be able to regulate the lacing, and keep it from becoming too dense or too light.

THE GROUND COLOUR

The only difference between the Golds and Silvers is in the ground colour, which in the former must be a rich, deep golden bay, and in the latter a pure clear silvery white. Many Golds are pale or washy in colour, and not a few Silvers show a creamy tint, which is most undesirable, even as it is most objectionable. In shape the Sebright should be short and compact, with a full prominent breast, the wings carried low, and the butts clipped close in to the sides, as slack carriage of wing is a great fault, and not only takes away from the bird's smartness, but also makes it look larger than it really is. Avoid birds with long backs ; this failing is a bad one, and one to which Sebright hens are somewhat prone. The head should be small and neat, the comb rosed, fairly broad in front and tapering off with a good leader ; the leader should not be carried high like that of the Rosecombs, but should follow the curve of the neck. The face of the cock should incline to the mulberry shade, especially round the eyes. A real mulberry faced cock is one of the things not yet attained ; in the pullets it is an indispensable feature. The lobes should be free from white, and not creased or folded ; the wattles small and neat, and follow the face in colour ; the beak should be short and stout and of horn colour ; the legs and feet slaty-blue ; the tail large, well spread, and carried high ; the cocks should be devoid of sickles. The plumage right through should be very clear in ground colour, and show no sign of being ticked or " peppery," as the wings and tail so often are. The lacing should be a rich, lustrous beetle-green black. The great thing is to get the lacing even all over the body, wing, and tail feather without breaks or unevenness ; that is, heavy on one part of the feather and finer " delicate " on another. The things to guard particularly against are " peppery " tails and flights, and lightness of lacing in the throat and breast. The feathers of the Sebright are shorter than those of most Bantams, and they are round in shape, even on the hackles, and not pointed like those of other breeds.

NOT PROLIFIC BREEDERS

Sebrights are not the most prolific breeders, therefore it is wise to use hens which are of fair size, and should you have a cock that is sickle-feathered, he will be worth breeding from, as such birds generally fertilise their eggs better than the normal or standard feathered cocks. In Golds the ground colour is apt to fade somewhat, and it is wise to keep a watchful eye on this property, when mating, and see that the cock especially is of a good sound bay colour ; if he inclines to the dark side, so much the better.

In breeding Sebrights in the early part of the year, only two hens or pullets should be run with the cock or cockerel, and later in the season not more than three. The great drawback to Sebright breeding is the fact that so many eggs are unfertile, especially in the early months. The best results are obtained by mating a cockerel to hens, as cockerels are generally more vigorous. April, May, and June are the best months to put eggs down, and when they hatch, the chicks require much care and attention during the first six weeks of their life. During that time they should be kept snug and dry, and fed rather more generously than is usual with Bantams.

CHAPTER XIII

MALAYS

THE Malay Bantam had at one time a fairly large following, but it can hardly be called a popular breed now. I have always understood that the late Mr. Entwisle was the originator of the Malay Bantam, but quite recently I read some notes written by Mr. Maunder, which said that they are one of our oldest breeds, and were exhibited in the middle of the last century. This statement I am inclined to doubt. It was in the eighties that I had my first Malay Bantams, they came from Mr. Entwisle, and I understood from him at that time that they were one of his modern introductions and the birds I bought were the first to win at the Palace and Birmingham.

In his book on Bantams, which was uncompleted when he passed away in 1892, Mr. Entwisle says it was after many years' labour that he succeeded in producing Malay Bantams. Now, if the statement is correct that Malay Bantams were shown in 1859, Mr. Entwisle could not have been the originator, as at that time he would only have been eighteen or nineteen years of age, and could not have produced them " after many years of labour."

Mr. Edgar Branford, in his work on the Malay Fowl and Malay Bantam, published in 1894, says it was about fourteen years before that time Mr. Entwisle began his operations in the production of the Malay Bantam. This agrees with what Mr. Entwisle himself told me when I purchased from him a pen of birds containing the first Malay cockerel that won a first prize at the Crystal Palace, and the hens which won at the Palace and Birmingham. Mr. Branford says that he had " many a time in past years wished there were such birds as Malay Bantams, and thought how attractive would be the shape, the swagger, and the scowl of the true

Malay combined with the saucy diminutiveness of the
Bantam." Had these birds been in existence and
winning in 1859, as Mr. Maunder says, how could Mr.
Branford, an old Malay breeder, have wished many a
time for their appearance? The evidence is against
Mr. Maunder and all in favour of Mr. Entwisle being
the originator of the Malay Bantam.

THE OLD TYPE AND THE NEW

The Malay Bantam of the eighties was altogether a
different bird to the Malay Bantam of to-day. At that
time the birds were Bantams, to-day one can hardly call
them such, for some birds are almost, if not quite, as
long in neck and limb as the large Malay Fowl. The
bird of the eighties possessed far more Malay character
than does the Malay Bantam of the present time.

Fanciers write and talk of the improvement of the
Malay, but I fail to see it. The birds nowadays are too
big altogether, and they have not the heavy scowling
heads which they had in the days when Mr. Entwisle
was breeding them. How modern breeders have produced the present elongated specimens I know not.
Neither can I undersand why they go on producing
them. They say that as soon as they began to reduce
them in size they lost the Malay character. If this is so,
they must have lost the art of breeding. Mr. Entwisle's
Malay Bantams were Bantams, and they were Malays
in character. In Mr. Entwisle's own words they were
" the exact counterparts of the large Malays," and
" only slightly larger than Game Bantams." There
is not a Malay Bantam winning to-day which answers
to this description. Whilst not an advocate of extreme
smallness in Bantams, I do say that a Bantam should
be a Bantam, and that cannot be said of the present-
day Malay Bantams.

WHAT IS WANTED

The colours most generally seen are Black-reds,
Whites, Spangles, Piles, Duckwings, Mottles, Reds,

and Blacks in the order given. The Black-reds are, however, the most largely bred ; they and the Spangles being as numerous, or more so than all the other colours put together. The Black-red cock should in colour resemble the Black-red Game ; he should be tall, upright in carriage of body, show the three curves (that is, neck, back and tail) distinctly, stand on good, sound legs and feet, the back toe being in a straight line with the front middle toe. The head should be broad and fairly short, with a heavy over-hanging eyebrow, the eye should be pearl or pale yellow in colour, although many are gravel or red. The beak should be strong, short, curved, and horn or yellow in colour. The neck should be long, well curved, the hackle feather being short and close. The shoulders should be square and prominent, the back curved, the breast deep and full, the tail carried low and drooping. The body should taper away from the breast, and be well cut up behind. The thighs should be long, strong, and muscular, the shanks stout, well scaled and orange in colour, the plumage short and hard. The weight should be about 2lb. 4ozs. to 2lb. 8ozs., the club standard 3½lb. This is really absurd, because it means that in due proportion a Malay Fowl should weigh 17½lb., whereas an 11lb. bird is a large one. There is the same lack of proportion in weight allowed for hens, the standard reads 3lb. How can birds of 3½ and 3lb. weight be termed Bantams ? The hens to be mated to the Black-red cock should be Partridge, Wheaten or Cinnamon in colour. They should resemble the cock in shape, plumage, and carriage, and weigh not more than from 1lb. 12ozs. to 2lb. In selecting both cocks and hens, see that they are hard and firm in flesh, and compact in body ; long feathered birds are useless as breeders.

THE WHITES

Whites should be clear white in colour, although many are somewhat creamy or strawy. Purity of colour is a great point. The Spangles should in colour resemble the Old English Game Spangles. Piles should be like unto Pile Game Bantams in colour, but few come near the standard, and the rules governing the mating of Pile Game Bantams should be observed in mating Pile Malay Bantams. The same applies to the Duckwings and other colours. At present, Malay Bantams are a long way behind Game Bantams in colour, because character is of so much more importance that breeders think little of colour ; this being so there is a big field open for the colourist.

Years ago the colours were much more distinct than they are at the present time, and one is often at a loss how to describe the colour of some of the birds shown.

WORK FOR THE EXPERIMENTALIST

At the present moment there is a big opening in Malay Bantams for a fancier of an experimental turn of mind, and if such a one would set himself the task of reducing the size of his birds, whilst not losing the Malay character, he would soon attain to the highest planes of the Fancy. Length of limb and neck are great features, but it should ever be remembered they should be proportionate with the size of the bird. It is foolish expecting a bird of 2lb. weight to have the same reach and curve as one which turns the scale at 3lb. Reduction of size and weight are what Malay Bantam breeders should bring about if they wish the bird to become more popular.

Malay Bantams are not great layers ; they are, however, good sitters, and make most excellent mothers. During the first month the chicks require careful treatment, owing to their slow feathering, and the fact that many of them are troubled with leg weakness. This may be corrected by the use of Parrish's Chemical Food in the drinking water. One good point about the Malay Bantam is that it does not require an elaborate show preparation, therefore it is a good breed for those whose time is limited. Little is required beyond the washing of the face, legs, and feet, and a good rub down of the plumage with a soft cloth or silk handkerchief. During the show season, good sound wheat is the best food, not forgetting a regular supply of fresh green vegetables of some kind if the birds are in enclosed runs.

CHAPTER XIV

INDIAN GAME

THESE, to lovers of colour and marking, are one of the most interesting varieties we have. It is not an old variety. The credit of producing it belongs to the late Mr. W. F. Entwisle. Although a fairly large number of fanciers keep Indian Game Bantams, it is not many shows which give them a place in their schedule yet when classes are provided they generally fill well, and few shows are there at which one or more Indian Game Bantams are not found in the variety class. The Indian Game Bantam should be the exact counterpart of the big Indian Game Fowl, and the cockerel should answer the following description :—Head, rather long and broad, somewhat beetle-browed ; neck of medium length and slightly arched, hackle short, just covering base of neck ; beak, horn colour, yellow, or horn striped with yellow, well curved, stout where set on head, giving bird a powerful appearance ; face, smooth and fine in texture, being dotted over with small feathers ; the face being of a rich red colour, also wattles and lobes ; comb, pea, i.e., three longitudinal ridges, the centre one being double height of those at the sides, small, closely set on head, and of a rich red colour ; eyebrows, very slightly beetle-browed, but not giving such a cruel expression as in the Malay ; eyes full and bold, varying from pale yellow to pale red ; body, very thick and compact, broad at shoulders, the shoulder butts showing prominently ; the body should taper towards tail ; elegance is required with substance ; back, flat and sloping ; breast, wide, fair depth, and prominent, well rounded ; wings, short and carried closely to body, well rounded at point, closely tucked at ends, carried rather high in front ; tail, medium length, with short, narrow, secondary

76

sickles and tail coverts, close, hard, and of a green glossy black colour, carriage drooping ; legs, strong and thick, thighs round and stout ; shank, medium length, and well scaled, the length of shank must be sufficient to give the bird a gamey appearance, but in no case should it be in any way stilty ; feet, strong and well-spread, toes long, straight, the back toe low and nearly flat on ground, nails well shaped ; general appearance, powerful, active, sprightly and vigorous, carriage upright, commanding and courageous ; plumage short, hard and close ; colour and marking, head, neck, breast, under fluff, thighs and tail black, with a rich green glossy black sheen or lustre, the base of the neck and tail hackles a little broken with bay or chestnut, which should be almost hidden by the body of the feathers ; shoulders and wing-bows green glossy black or beetle-green, slightly broken with bay or chestnut in the centre of the feather or shaft ; tail coverts green glossy black or beetle-green, slightly broken with bay or chestnut in the base of the shaft ; back feathers green glossy black or beetle-green, also touched on the fine fronds at the end of the feathers with bay or chestnut, which gives the sheen so much desired. When the wing is closed there is a triangular patch of bay or chestnut formed of the secondaries, which are green glossy black or beetle-green on the inner, and bay or chestnut on the outer web, which when closed show only the bay in a solid triangle. The primaries, ten in number, are curved and of a deep black, except for a narrow lacing on the outer web of a light chestnut ; shanks and feet rich yellow or orange colour. Weight, about 28 to 32 ounces.

BEAUTY OF THE HENS

The hen is like unto the cock in head, neck, beak, face, comb, eyes, body, back, breast, wings, legs, shanks and feet. Tail, rather short, close, carried low, but somewhat higher than cock's. In colour the hen is quite different to the cock. The ground colour is chestnut brown, nut brown, or mahogany brown; head, hackle, and throat green glossy black, or beetle-green. The pointed hackle that lies under the neck feathers green glossy black, or beetle-green with a bay or chestnut centre mark; the breast commencing on the lower part of the throat should show double lacing of a rich bay or chestnut, the inner or double lacing being most distinct; the belly and thighs are marked somewhat similarly, running off into a mixture of indistinct markings under the vent. The feathers of the shoulders and back are somewhat smaller, enlarging towards the tail coverts, and are similarly marked with the double lacing; the marking on the wing-bows and shoulders running down to the waist is the most distinct of all, with the same kind of double lacing, and often in the best specimens there is an additional mark enclosing the base of the shaft of the feather and running to a point in the second or inner lacing. The tail coverts are seldom as distinctly marked. The primary or flight feathers are black, except on the inner web, which are a little coloured or peppered with a light chestnut; the secondaries are black on the inner web, while the outer web is in keeping with the general ground colour, and edged with a delicate lacing of green glossy black, or beetle-green; the wing coverts, which form the bar, are laced like those of the body, and often a little peppered. Weight, 24ozs. to 28ozs. The above description is based on the Indian Game Club standard. If Indian Game Bantams are bred to less weight than this, much of the character is lost. Breed characteristics, in my opinion, are far more valuable than the reduction of a few ounces in weight. The Indian Game Fowl is a large bird, and the Indian Game Bantam should be in proportion. Some Indian Game Bantam breeders are inclined to pay more attention to size than breed character, hence my warning.

THE BREEDING PENS

In breeding it is absolutely necessary to breed from two distinct pens for cockerels and pullets.

Therefore, if circumstances do not permit of keeping two distinct strains of birds, I would say decide whether cockerel breeding or pullet breeding shall be your aim, and mate your pen accordingly. Taking the cockerel breeding pen first, choose a cock or cockerel, the former for choice, as nearly approaching the standard of perfection as possible. He must be of true Indian Game character and shape, and sound in colour—without these two requisites he is worthless for cock breeding. When you have secured these properties, the smaller the bird the better, but in comparison with true shape and soundness of colour, size, as I have previously said, should be a very secondary consideration. To mate with this cock secure pullets of true shape and quite free from any trace of red or rusty colour in hackle, and if possible with good sound wing bays. Of these points, shape and breed character are by far the most important, and without this cockerel breeding pullets are useless. To secure all the necessary points in one bird is hard, but when such a one is found she is invaluable. After shape and character, and colour of hackle and wing bays, size may be considered, but not before. Hens or pullets that are deficient in lacing are best for cockerel breeding.

In pullet breeding one has to proceed on totally different lines, as the question of lacing is all-important, and it is often a matter of difficulty to secure the right cock or cockerel. Buying a cock or cockerel for this purpose is always more or less of a lottery, everything depending upon how the bird is bred. He must come from a pullet breeding strain ; therefore the best way to start pullet breeding is to place yourself in the hands of a reliable breeder and try what he sends you. It is quite possible the bird may be quite the reverse of a show bird. He will very likely show red in both neck and saddle hackle, be more or less laced on breast, and to some extent on the wings. Once a strain for pullet breeding is established, the real secret lies in examining all the cockerels bred from the pullet breeding pen when in their chicken feathers, marking all the best laced ones, and making a final selection when full growth is attained, choosing for breeding the birds excelling in shape and character, shortness and hardness of feather. Possessed of these qualifications, and smallness of size—the smaller the better—they should prove themselves most valuable as pullet breeders. The cock or cockerel having been selected, mate with him the best exhibition hens or pullets that can be found ; hens, if you can get them, as you may be sure, if your hens are sound in colour, that they will breed pullets not likely to fade in colour in their second year (many good pullets go light in colour as they get older). None but good show hens or pullets should be used in the pullet-breeding pens ; hens washy in colour or indistinct in lacing or single laced cannot be expected to breed pullets well laced and sound in colour, and these two points are most essential in exhibition pullets. One thing must ever be remembered—on no account use either cocks or hens for breeding that are long or soft in feather.

Being a hard-feathered bird, the Indian Game Bantam requires hard feeding, and sound wheat is the best. They must not be overfed, because a bird that is allowed to become gross and fat in body is very soon soft in feather. If in confined runs, they should be given a little green food every day.

Jubilee Indian Game Bantams are gradually making headway. The lacing of the hens has been much improved, as has the type of both sexes, but thus far the great difficulty has been to secure clearness of colour in the cocks. My own opinion is that if those interested would decide that both sexes should be laced the Jubilee would make a big jump in popular favour.

CHAPTER XV

MINORCAS, LEGHORNS, ANDALUSIANS AND SPANISH

MINORCAS

ALL of these are yet in a state resembling suspended animation. They are all in the land, but they do not seem to make any headway. So far as the Minorcas are concerned there should not be any great difficulty in breeding them, even if one had to start clean away and build up—or should it be down?—a strain. The *modus operandi* would be to select a very small Minorca cock, one with a nice and straight comb and fair amount of lobe, and mate him to rather large Black Rosecomb Bantam hens. They should be mated rather late in the season. The cockerels bred from this cross should not be bred from, they should be killed, but the pullets showing the most Minorca character should be mated the following season to their sire. Most of the first season chicks it is possible would have rose combs, but from the second year's breeding there should be a fair number with single combs. In the third season I should mate up some of the second season cockerels with their sisters of that and the previous year, making careful selection of the chicks, and in the fourth mating expect to have something very near to the standard.

During the last few years Minorcas have been more largely bred, and there would not be much difficulty in purchasing a pen, but even so much building up would be needed, as really good birds are few and far between.

LEGHORNS

Leghorn Bantams are almost unknown. I saw some a few years back in the possession of a well-known breeder of Black Leghorns. To breed White or Black Leghorn Bantams I should be inclined to experiment in two different directions. In one pen I should use a very small White, or Black, Leghorn cock and mate him to White or Black or Rosecomb hens of good size, birds that one would reject as too large if breeding Rosecombs, and proceed as I have said in producing Minorca Bantams. Another pen I should make up with a small White or Black Leghorn cock and some plain feathered hens bred from Frizzle Bantams. In this case the chief difficulty to overcome would be the red lobe which the Frizzles possess. Still, I believe this would be more easily eradicated than the rose comb, whilst one would start right away with good yellow legs and feet, and this means a lot.

In breeding Buff Leghorn Bantams one pen could be made up with a small Buff Leghorn cock and some White Rosecomb hens, and another with a Buff Leghorn cock and some plain feathered hens from White Frizzles. For the breeding of Brown Leghorn Bantams I should advise a pen made up of a Brown Leghorn cock, and some yellow-legged Partridge Old English Game Bantam hens, proceeding in each case on the lines suggested for the Minorcas. In this case the results should be most satisfactory. Duckwings and Piles might also be produced in the same manner by selecting a Leghorn cock of the character desired and using Old English Game Bantam hens.

ANDALUSIANS

These have been bred and shown now for quite a number of years, and very pretty they are when they approach anything near to the proper colour of the Andalusian, but the majority I have seen have failed in this great essential. Still, with the material ready to hand and a few years' careful breeding it should not be at all difficult to produce something far better than the birds of to-day.

It may be that the fact of Andalusian Bantams not breeding true to colour has had something to do with their unpopularity, even as it has hindered the progress of their larger brethren. In this, however, much depends upon strain, and the care with which the birds are mated. The best way to proceed is to select a cock or cockerel sound in his blue both on top and under, as regular and even as possible in his lacing, and possessing rich bright glossy black hackles and wing bow, and mate him to hens or pullets of a light clear shade of blue but yet clearly and distinctly laced. Such a pen should produce a fair percentage of good blue chickens. The great failing to-day is in the colour, the birds are not clear enough in their blue, and this is caused by breeding from birds which are smudgy in colour, therefore I advocate a good clear bright blue as the ground colour of all birds used for breeding.

In weight Andalusian Bantams should be about the same as Leghorn Bantams.

SPANISH

A few years ago several very nice Spanish Bantams made their appearance in the show pen, birds that were indeed miniature Spanish, possessing beautiful long, smooth, open, white faces, grand shape, and beautiful colour and feather. I am not an admirer of the large Spanish Fowl, but I was most captivated with these Bantams. They were so smart and stylish in body, so rich and glossy in their plumage, and had a lovely kid-like texture of face. The start having been made, it should not be at all difficult to keep up the characteristics of the breed, but as it must of necessity be some time before birds of this breed will be plentiful, those who fancy Spanish Bantams should have a try at producing them, that is, if they fail to purchase the ready-made article. If they set about making their own strain I should advise the use of a small Spanish cock and some large Black Rosecomb hens, and then work on the same lines as advised for Minorca Bantams.

Spanish need careful feeding, and must never be given much heating or stimulating food, or the beauty of the face and lobes will at once be spoilt ; bread and milk, rice boiled in milk, hard rice, wheat and canary seed make good feeding. Exhibition birds need also to be protected from the weather so as to preserve the beauty of their faces and lobes, but should be allowed plenty of fresh air, grit, and green food. Given ordinary care and attention they will do well. The size and weight should be about the same as in Leghorns and Andalusians.

CHAPTER XVI

NANKINS, BURMESE, SULTANS, JAPANESE, RUMPLESS, AND POLISH

NANKINS

Nankins are one of the oldest breeds of Bantams known to English fanciers, and have been largely used in the production of many of the other breeds which we have, yet the breed seems to have been completely lost.

The Nankins resembled Rosecombs very much in shape and style ; in colour they were buff, the cock being richer and deeper in tone than the hen, approaching unto chestnut, with a good flowing tail of a darker hue, and generally showing black. The hen in body was nearer the colour of Buff Pekins, with a darker tail shading off from brown into black at the extremity ; the inner half of the primary feathers of both cock and hen were also black. Legs, slate blue, face, comb and wattles bright red ; both single and rose combed birds used to be shown.

Anyone wishing to produce them might try the effect of crossing a Gold Sebright cock with Wheaten Old English Game and Rosecomb hens, and then resorting to careful in-breeding. The colour might be obtained from the Sebright cock and Old English hens, and the shape and style from the Rosecombs. It would be a task requiring considerable patience, but the result would fully compensate the breeder.

BURMESE

This is another variety which seems to have died out. The Burmese was very heavily crested, with a small straight single comb in front of its crest ; it was long in wing, very heavily feathered on its legs and in tail, the sickles of which were wonderful in their length ;   the legs were short, so short that the bird seemed to shuffle rather than walk ;   the legs, excepting   in   blacks, were yellow.   The late Mr. Entwisle had some Burmese years ago in various colours—whites, browns, blacks, greys, and speckled.

SULTANS

Sultan Bantams were amongst the productions of the late Mr. Entwisle, but they seem to have quite died out. Mr. Entwisle produced them by crossing a small Sultan cock with White Polish Bantam hens and White Booted Bantam hens, and then in-breeding the progeny.   In the second season he mated a Sultan-Booted pullet, and a Sultan-Polish pullet back to their sire, and a Sultan-Polish cockerel to Sultan-Booted pullets.   From the last pen he only saved the pullets, killing all the cockerels. The next season's cross was a three-quarter Sultan and quarter-Booted cockerel with some of the pullets from the Sultan-Polish cockerel and the Sultan-Booted pullets, and from these he bred birds which were very small in size and almost perfect in Sultan Points, and made a strain of birds which won prizes at all the leading shows.

JAPANESE

These quaint little chaps have been known to English fanciers for nearly 50 years.   In shape and general character they differ from any other Bantams known to English breeders, but in their shortness of leg and shuffling gait they bear some resemblance to the Burmese.   They are very heavily feathered and look much larger than they really are.   They are hardy and breed very true to character—which points to a long ancestry in their Eastern home.

There are several colours—Whites, Blacks, Blues, Buffs, Greys, Black-reds, Browns, Mottles, and Black-tailed Whites.   In all colours the face, comb, wattles, and lobes are bright red, the combs being single, thin in substance and evenly serrated ; the beak, legs and feet are yellow. They are very short in the leg and thigh, the body almost touching the ground ; this lowness of body is a great point, the shorter the leg, and the lower the body the more valuable the bird. The wings are long and carried low, touching the ground ; the tail is large and full, and carried very erect, the sickles almost touching the head.

The Whites are pure white right through, the Black-tailed Whites are white in body with a black tail, the sickles being edged with white ; the upper and outer feather of the wing is white but black in the inner web. The Blacks are a rich lustrous solid black throughout. The Grey cock has silvery white hackles and is white on back and wing bow, the ground colour being black ; the hen is black, finely laced with silvery white. The Mottles are black and white splashed. The Buffs should be a sound buff throughout, but many of them are black in flights and tail. The Browns are a richer, deeper colour than the Buffs, and also show black in the flights and tail. The Black-reds have black breasts, flights and tail, the other portions of the plumage being a rich golden brown. In weight the cocks are about 1lb. 2oz. to 1lb. 6oz., whilst the hens run from 14ozs. to 18oz.

The Japs lay fairly well, are good sitters, and most excellent mothers. The chicks are fairly hardy, not over difficult to rear, and if kept dry, feather quickly and grow well.

RUMPLESS

Rumpless Bantams are not often met with in England but they are fairly common in the Isle of Man. The Rumpless is what the Mendelians would term a " domi-nant," for it seems to have stamped itself upon Bantams of all sorts, shapes and sizes, but they all seem to have the same peculiar style, carrying themselves very erect, and looking as though they would almost topple over backwards. This is caused by the fact that the spine is deficient in the final vertebrae. This fact has been proved by dissection. Mr. W. B. Tegetmeier and the late Charles Darwin conducted a series of experiments years ago dealing with the subject of variation in animals, and in the course of such proved how dominant is the Rumpless, it only needing two crosses to make perfect Tailless Polish, and the same to produce Rumpless Nankin Bantams.

Seeing that they are such oddities and so quaint in appearance and movement it seems strange that they have never become popular in England.

POLISH

This is another of the varieties for which we are indebted to the unflagging love of experiment and creation which dominated the late W. F. Entwisle, who in his time produced and exhibited no less than ten different colours of Polish Bantams—White, Black, Buff, Gold, Silver, Creamy, Cuckoo, Blue, White-crested Black, and White-crested Blue. Many of these have unfortunately been allowed to disappear, and it is very seldom that we have seen anything except Whites, White-crested Blacks, and an occasional Buff, Gold or Silver. In his experiments to produce the Polish, Mr. Entwisle used Gold and Silver Sebright and Black and White Rosecomb Bantams, Gold, Silver, White, Black, and White-crested Black Polish. In producing Golds and Silvers he used Sebright hens, with small Polish cocks of the same colours, and Rosecomb hens with White-crested Black Polish to produce the Bantams of these colours, and great as were the difficulties which he had to surmount, he has placed it on record that in the sixth year he bred Gold Polish Bantams which were equal to winning first prizes and a silver cup. To-day the best Polish Bantams are to be found in Holland.

GOLDS AND SILVERS

It seems strange that whilst in the Polish Fowl the Golds and Silvers have ever been the most popular, that in the Bantams the self colours find most favour. Yet even they are not very popular. Why, it seems hard to say, for they are very attractive. The only reason that they do not make greater advance is due, I am inclined to think, to the fact that even in Bantams the commercial spirit of the Fancy is a dominant factor, and that we have not so many breeders nowadays who keep birds for pure love of the hobby. This being so, crested birds, owing to the trouble entailed in keeping the crests in good order, have few followers.

THE SELF COLOURS

In the self colours the great feature next to shape and size of crest is purity of colour, whilst in the others regularity of marking takes the place of colour. Anyone wishing for something quaint, yet at the same time beautiful and attractive, should try their hand at the raising of Polish Bantams. There is a good opening in this variety for fanciers who love the unique, and that which is difficult to produce.

One thing to remember above all others in the breeding of Polish Bantams is never to put in the breeding pen birds which are hollow-fronted, or which have the crest set too far back on the head, as these are failings which are very difficult to eradicate. The crest should be very full and round, especially in front, the fuller the front the more valuable the bird, both as an exhibition specimen and as a breeder.

OF HARDY CONSTITUTION

Polish Bantams are fairly hardy and of good constitution, but they need good housing. They must also be well looked after as regards lice, as their crest is a hindrance to them in preening their plumage, and they cannot rid themselves of vermin so easily as non-crested birds. They should not be allowed out too early in the morning, neither should they be let run in long, wet grass. In early spring and late autumn they should be kept indoors when it is wet, for if their crests are allowed to become sodden with the rain they are apt to get chilled, contract colds and roup, which lead to a lot of trouble and often cause death. Given proper treatment and good houses Polish Bantams will thrive and do well.

CHAPTER XVII

WYANDOTTES

THE PARTRIDGE

THESE are amongst the latest of the miniatures to be produced. The Wyandotte lends itself well to reduction, and it is really wonderful what a state of perfection the miniature Wyandotte have reached.

The Partridge was the first of the Wyandotte Bantams to appear, and thus I give them pride of place here. Taking the cockerels first, the hackle is a great feature in a first-class bird. This should be of a rich golden orange colour, with a green-black stripe down the centre of each feather. It is important that this striping should be very clear and distinct. It should not run to the extreme tip of the feather or the hackle will look cloudy or sooty. The saddle hackle should match the neck hackle, but generally speaking it is a shade or two darker in colour. In the ideal bird the two should correspond both in colour and striping. The back should be a rich bright red of a darkish shade, but not so dark as to be mahogany or dark red. The colour should be clear and solid, not mixed with black. The wing should be a rich green-black without any sign of mossiness or blurring. The breast and thighs should be rich green-black, solid and deep without any signs of rustiness or red ticking. The flights should be solid black, free from grey or white, and the tail a rich beetle-green black. Many birds fail in wings and tail, the feathers showing grey or white when opened out.

Exhibition pullets should have a clearly pencilled golden hackle, the pencilling being very fine. The body colour should be a soft light brown, perfectly even and free from yellow, reddish, or mahogany tinge. Every feather from the throat to the tail should be clearly and finely pencilled with rich green-black pencilling. The shaft of every feather should be black, and the bands across the web clear, distinct, and uniform, not broken or showing signs of ticking. The more uniform the pencilling, the more valuable the bird, especially if the fluff is well pencilled, as this is where the majority fail. In regard to this point it must not be forgotten that hens are invariably superior in pencilling to pullets.

In breeding Partridges double mating is imperative. Those who breed cockerels will need to select as the head of their pen a bird such as I have before described, in a word, a good exhibition bird. To him should be mated hens or pullets of good size and shape with dark body colour as free from pencilling as possible except upon the hackle, and this should be as nearly as possible like the cock's hackle, that is, rich golden colour with a well defined black stripe. Avoid birds which show pencilling in the hackle, or which are dark or muddy coloured in hackle. Look well to the colour of legs, avoid those that are dark, and select those coming nearest to the standard of rich golden orange.

In mating up a pullet breeding pen one goes on different lines to those pursued in cockerel breeding. The first consideration is the hens or pullets. These must, if not actually good exhibition specimens, come somewhere near to exhibition form. The more perfect they are the more likelihood is there of their progeny being up to exhibition form. The cockerel for pullet breeding is a totally different bird to the one required for cockerel breeding. In purchasing such a cockerel one has to trust the seller, because often a likely looking pullet breeder is not always what he appears to be, and selecting by appearance is a very risky business. He should be of a darker shade than the cockerel breeder ; if there are signs of pencilling they are of value, and he should not be so bright in colour or hackle. The breast should be well mottled with red feathers, and his wing should show signs of lacing, as may his tail. Much, however, depends upon strain, and it often happens that an unlikely looking bird for the purpose turns out to be one of the best pullet producers, therefore one can only generalise in describing a pullet breeding cockerel.

The faults in Partridges which are most prevalent are whiteness in lobe, lightness of eye, few possessing the rich blood-red eye which is so much desired. The hackle striping is often pale and dull in colour, and the hackle itself is not sound in colour, being either too light, too dark, or blotchy. In cockerels the breast and fluff is often tinged with red, whilst the top colour is generally much too dark. The pullets are too dark in legs, and many also fail in colour, being too red or foxy. A very general fault is lack of pencilling on fluff, whilst some birds are not sound in pencilling on the cushion, showing signs of ticking, that is the dark bands being broken by the ground colour. In breeding many birds come showing white, therefore those who purchase eggs must not blame the seller when this happens.

THE SILVER PENCILLED

The breeder of Silver Pencils is confronted with almost the same problems and difficulties as the breeder of Partridges. From a colour point of view there are few birds more beautiful than the Silver-pencilled. The neck hackle of the cockerel should be a clear silvery white, free from creaminess or straw colour ; each feather should have a rich green-black stripe running down the centre, reaching almost, but not quite, to the tip. The saddle hackle should be full and abundant, and match the neck hackle in colour and striping ; the more solid and distinct the striping, the more valuable. The wing bow and butts should be silvery white, without the slightest trace of any other colour. The rest of the plumage should be a rich green-black showing plenty of sheen.

The exhibition pullet should have a hackle similar to the exhibition cockerel, although many show a tendency to pencilling, especially when the body pencilling is extra good. The body colour should be a soft silvery grey, with every feather regularly and finely pencilled with clear green-black bands. This pencilling should start at the throat, go down the breast and thighs, and over the top of the body ; the two top feathers of the tail should also show it, the rest of the tail being black.

In mating the Silver-pencilled the same rules must be observed as in the Partridges. Silver-pencilled breeders find much difficulty in keeping up the quality of the pencilling, which seems to be far weaker than that of the Partridges. Another great difficulty is colour, many of the pullets exhibiting a tendency to go brown, and with age this failing gets worse, so much so, that some birds after their first adult moult are quite brown and show scarcely any silver colour. To counteract this failing, which in the opinion of some has been brought about by crossing with the Partridges, breeders should select their breeding stock strongly for colour, casting on one side any bird which fails in this respect, no matter how good it may be in other properties. Colour being such an important property in the Silver-pencilled it will pay to sacrifice other points for a season or two until colour has not only been improved, but also fastened in the strain.

Silver-pencilled Wyandotte Bantams should, like other delicately coloured birds, be given plenty of shade after they reach the age of five months, and even during early chickenhood they will be none the worse for it, but they should not be penned up for that purpose until they are four or five months old. If birds are allowed to run in exposed situations after they are five months old their plumage will become tanned.

WHITES

The general properties in the White are the same as in the other colours, its distinctive feature being its colour, which should be a pure dead white throughout, both top and underneath, but there are some which are somewhat sappy or creamy, especially the cockerels. If great care is used in the selection of breeding stock the colour may be much improved. It does not do to condemn white chickens too early, as in some cases birds which are sappy and creamy in their first feathers moult out well. Birds that are intended for breeding should not be selected until they have moulted right through. They can still be further examined and re-selected so to speak when mating-up time comes along. Thus by the double process of selection none but the purest coloured birds will get into the breeding pens. As a general rule the cocks have most to say where colour is concerned, and therefore, extra care should be given to the selection of the cocks and cockerels.

Bad top colour may not be natural, but may be the result of exposure to the sun and weather. This can easily be ascertained by lifting the feathers and examining the under-colour. If the quills and web of the feathers near the body are sound and pure white you need have no hesitation in putting down the bad outside appearance to the weather. One point in connection with Whites which is worthy of note is that it often happens that a bird which is sappy or creamy in its first season often moults out the second year with a coat of perfect purity.

Breeders of Whites have not to contend with the difficulties of marking, lacing, etc.—size and shape become of greater importance, and the breeder who in addition to possessing birds pure in colour pays extra attention to these points, not overlooking the other breed characteristics, is certain to reap a fair share of the honours of the show pen.

THE COLUMBIAN

The Columbian bears the same relationship to the Silver-pencilled as the Light Brahma does to the Dark Brahma. The principal difficulty which breeders have thus far had to encounter has been that of hackle colour. Birds good in body plumage, shape, and size, have been produced, but they have failed in hackle and tail, particularly the former. Yet it should not be so, because if breeding is followed on correct lines the colour of body and hackle ought each to improve automatically. That the Columbian is one of the most strikingly beautiful members of a most handsome family no one will deny. The markings of the Columbian Wyandotte Bantam are similar to those of the Light Brahma Bantam, and these seen in contrast with the lovely clear pure body colour and bright orange-yellow legs make a picture that must appeal at once to those who have the artistic faculties well developed.

The chief difficulty in breeding Columbians is to obtain a sufficient amount of pencilling or marking in the hackle without producing dark feathers in other places where they are not wanted. The natural tendency is for the hackle to come lighter and lighter, therefore much thought must be given to this point, upon which so much of the beauty of the variety depends. A cockerel for breeding should have the hackle striping very clear and distinct, be sound in body colour, and in all respects come as near the ideal as possible. Such a bird mated to hens light in hackle will produce cockerels which should come somewhere near to standard requirements. For pullet breeding the hens or pullets used should be good exhibition birds, or those which have an excess of colour in the hackle ; the cockerel need not be an exhibition bird, but one with narrow yet very distinct hackle striping.

It is possible to breed both cockerels and pullets from the same pen, but the double mating gives the best results, and the percentage of wasters is not so large. If double mating is not convenient and only one pen can be used, then the cockerel heading the pen should be as near to the standard required as is possible, whilst the hens, or pullets may be exhibition birds, or approaching thereto. They must not be too light in their marking, neither must they be too dark, as very heavily marked hens or pullets produce cockerels far too dark, and faintly marked ones produce pullets too light and washy in hackle. In single mating the disappointments will be more frequent than in double mating, yet those who like to breed both sexes from the one pen, owing to their not having time or accommodation, may do so and feel assured that they will meet with a fair measure of success if they are careful in the selection of their original breeding birds.

Columbians vary in under-colour, and the standard allows it to be so, saying they may be slate, white, or bluish white. This under-colour has much to say in the breeding results. If birds dark in under-colour are mated together, then an excess of hackle colour is likely to become general, with dark splashes and blotches of body colour. On the other hand, if only light or white under-colour birds are mated, then, although the cockerels may be near the standard, the pullets will be too light and washy in hackles. In single mating, therefore, if the cockerel used is dark in under-colour his mates should not be dark, or no good cockerels will be obtained from the mating. If they are dead white, then the pullets will not have enough marking. This being so, whenever there is dark under-colour on one side, the medium or bluish-white under-colour should be found in the other.

In general breed characteristics the Columbian follows all the other Wyandotte Bantams, in others, it should answer to the following. Taking the cockerels first we want the head feather to be a clear silvery white, with neck hackle of the same colour, but each feather to be sharply and distinctly marked down the middle with a rich green-black stripe ; this stripe must not extend beyond the centre ; the outer edges and tip of each feather must be pure silvery white. The saddle hackle must be white. The tail should be full and of a rich green-black colour, the outer feathers being edged or laced with white ; the secondaries should be white on the outer edge and black on the inner ; the rest of the body should be pure white, free from blotches or ticking ; the under-colour may be white, bluish-white, or grey.

The pullets should follow the cocks in head colour ; the neck hackle should be composed of bright green-black feathers entirely surrounded with a silvery white margin. The tail should be rich green-black, with the two top feathers laced with white. The primary wing flights should be black, or black laced with white, and the secondaries white on the outer edge and black on the

G

inner. The rest of the body must be pure white, with the same latitude in under-colour as in the cockerels.

In experimenting some have used the Light Brahma Bantam, and although such a system has many drawbacks, it has also many advantages. The feathered legs may, by careful selection, be got rid of in a few years, whilst the wonderful improvement in hackle and tail, to say nothing of body colour, more than compensates for the disadvantages.

BLUES

The Blue Wyandotte Bantam is as yet in a very experimental state, and the Fancy is undecided even in the big Wyandottes as to what the Blue shall be, some contending for a self-colour, whilst others declare such to be impossible of attainment. These latter seek to produce a bird blue in body but possessing dark hackles. The dark hackled birds are richer and deeper in body tone than the clear hackled birds, and the colour is more lasting, whilst many of the lighter coloured birds present a very washed-out looking appearance, and in some cases hardly merit the designation of blue, being neither more nor less than smoky whites. The richer coloured birds do present more contrast, therefore, are more pleasing to the eye, and contrasts which blend and harmonise are essentially more beautiful than something which appears to be of one faded hue. Breeders have used the Andalusian Bantam in the making of the Blue Wyandotte Bantam, and the consequence is that all the birds show more or less lacing. It is possible that by a judicious use of the white and black blood in the strains now existent advance would be made in the clearing out of the lacing, but little headway will be made unless those who are interested agree that the birds shall possess dark hackles, and further decide that the birds shall be laced.

BLACKS

The Black Wyandotte Bantam compares favourably with other members of the family in shape, size, head, and colour properties, especially in pullets ; the two weak points are lack of soundness in under-colour in the cockerels and sooty legs in the pullets. The cockerels possess rich top colour with plenty of beetle-green sheen ; they are also most excellent in leg colour, but when one comes to examine them carefully very few are found sound in under-colour, tail, and flights. If we go in for double mating in Black Wyandottes, this difficulty, as also that of the dusky legs in the pullets, will be quickly overcome. It is my opinion that by careful selection we shall be able to overcome these difficulties, and that soundness of under-colour and purity of leg colour will go hand-in-hand. In fact, I have seen birds in breeding pens, both cockerels and pullets, which, whilst thoroughly sound in under-colour, flights, and tail, have clear yellow legs.

We have not got far enough yet with the variety for anyone to lay down dogmatic and arbitrary rules as to breeding. Some breeders go so far as to say that it is impossible to breed the Blacks from sound coloured birds on each side, but this is a fallacy. Double mating would, of course, simplify matters greatly, but it would give us a larger percentage of birds which are useless, owing to the small demand which exists for pullet-breeding cockerels. I am not an advocate for double mating, but would urge breeders to make judicious selection, watching the birds, noting carefully the points in the progeny year by year, and to gradually improve the two points mentioned. Experiments with white blood have convinced me that for securing purity of leg colour, and increasing the depth and richness of the colour, the progressive breeder must mix his black blood with a little white occasionally.

BLUE-LACED

The ground colour of the Blue-laced should be bay, with clear blue lacing, blue wing bars, and a blue stripe in the hackle feather. It is possible to breed both sexes from one pen, but far quicker and surer will be the results if double mating is resorted to. To breed high-class cockerels select a cock or cockerel as sound as possible in ground colour, and carrying nice open clearly defined regular lacing on his breast. Look well to the bars, these are important, and add greatly to the appearance of a bird, and as nice clear wing bars are somewhat difficult of attainment particular attention should be given to the selection of the head of the exhibition cockerel breeding pen. It will not be easy to find a bird which excels in colour, lacing, and wing bars, therefore breeders must get one approaching to the standard. All birds fail in some point or other, but the one which comes nearest to the exhibition ideal is the bird to place at the head of the pen for cockerel breeding. The pullets or hens selected to mate with such a bird should be as sound as possible in hackle and body colour ; in lacing they may be on the close or heavy side, but they should have, above all things, a good solid tail. That is if such can be found. At present all the hens show a certain amount of ticking or mossiness. The legs of both cocks and hens in the cockerel pen should be as clean and free from sootiness as it is possible to get them. On the questions of type and size it may be taken as a sound principle that hens influence shape more than cocks, whilst the latter have the greater say in reference to size. Therefore, in improving type, the best shaped hens must be used, and in breeding small birds, only small cocks or cockerels should be mated.

In breeding for pullets the cock or cockerel should be more heavily laced than the one used for breeding cockerels, but although more heavily laced he should be pure in ground colour. Don't breed with a smutty dirty coloured cockerel if you can in any way avoid. Purity of ground colour is of the greatest consideration, whether one be breeding for cockerels or pullets. The hackles and tail of the pullet breeder should be sound, and his wing bars clear, although they may be more heavy than in the cockerel breeder. The hens or pullets used for pullet breeding must come as near to the exhibition standard as it is possible to get them.

The Blue-laced Wyandotte Bantam should answer to the following description. Taking the cockerel first, the head and hackle should be bright bay, with a distinct blue stripe down the centre of each feather, the hackle free from black tips and black round the edging. The back and wings should be rich bay, free from black or smutty blue. The shoulders, back and wing-bow all rich bay. Wing-bars : Laced blue and well defined. Saddle hackles, similar to neck. Breast, rich bay, with well defined blue lacing, free from double or outer lacing, regular from throat to back of thighs, free from black or smutty lacing. Fluff, blue, powdered with gold. Tail, solid blue, free from black or white. The head and neck feathers of the hen should be bright bay, with a distinct blue stripe down centre of each feather. Breast all black ; wings, thighs, and cushion, rich bay, regularly laced, with well-defined blue-lacing, free from double or outer lacing, the lacing to extend to back of thigh into the fluff. Tail, solid blue.

BUFF-LACED

The buff-laced, like the blue-laced, are sweetly pretty even as they are difficult to breed. Like the large buff-laced, they are closely allied to the blue-laced, and sports between the two are somewhat frequent. In fact I have known the blue-laced when crossed with whites to produce some very nice buff-laced. In the buff-laced, as in the blue-laced, double mating is the surest and swiftest road to the desired goal. Therefore in cockerel breeding I advise the selection of a bird as the head of the pen which comes near to the standard of perfection for exhibition cockerels. He should be mated to hens of sound buff top colour, with even regular breast lacing ; if they are somewhat heavy in lacing on top it will be no detriment, but rather an advantage, providing the lacing is even and clear, the under-colour and tail as white as possible. In breeding for pullets the cock or cockerel used should be sound in colour right through and somewhat heavily laced, but his mates should come as near as possible to the exhibition standard.

The high-class buff-laced should approach near to the following description. Taking the cock first his head should be a nice rich buff, the neck and saddle hackles a good rich buff, with white stripe down centre of each feather ;   breast and thighs, rich buff, with clear and regular white lacing ;   under-colour white ;   back, shoulders and wing-bow all rich solid buff, of same shade as buff in saddle.   Wing bars laced with pure white and well defined.   Secondaries, white on the inner web, outer web rich buff-laced and white ;   tail and under-colour, white.

The exhibition pullet should be similar to the cockerel in colour of head and neck, her breast, back, and wings should be rich buff with clear regular white lacing. Secondaries, buff with neat white lacing on outer web. Fluff and tail white ;   the lacing on the cushion may continue into the tail coverts.

BUFFS

These are likely to become popular when better known, and improved in colour.   They should be of a rich golden buff hue, without any sign of mealiness, or on the other hand a dark or reddish hue.   There is considerable variation to-day in the colour, some being richer than others, but upon one point, evenness, all breeders are agreed.   The colour should extend right through the bird, that is all over the body and down to the roots of the feathers, " Buff to the skin," is an oft-heard expression, and is an accurate description of what a good Buff should be.

The faults most general in cockerels are dark coloured, shoulders, light under-colour, sooty or dark hackles, black and white feathers in the tail.   The pullets come more even in colour and in them the prevailing faults are sooty and ticked hackles, mealiness of body colour, and peppery tails.   The greatest fault is mealiness, as it betokens a lack of the essential buff colouring matter in the blood, and this fault is one that needs constant watching, as the Buffs generally show a disposition to breed chickens lighter than the parent stock.

In selecting Buffs for breeding, the first consideration in both sexes should be soundness of colour—buff to the skin. Cocks which are grey or white in flights and tail should never be chosen, but a bird which is too dark in body for exhibition, or dark in flights or tail may be, as he will correct the tendency to lightness of colour. An otherwise good bird need not be discarded even if he shows a slight amount of black in the tail, although the more even and pure in colour he is the better. The hens or pullets should, however, be sound not only in body feather, but also in flights and tails.

CHAPTER XVIII

PEKINS

THE Pekin Bantam is not by any means a modern production. It has been known in this country for some sixty years, and is undoubtedly of very ancient lineage, having been cultivated in China, the home of the Cochin, for ages before it was known in England. The most fashionable colours are Buffs, Blacks, and Whites, followed by Partridges and Cuckoos, whilst on the Continent I have seen Mottles and Spangles.

The original importations were Buffs, but they were very different, both in colour and shape, to the present day Buffs. The cocks were a rich dark cinnamon hue, with white and straw coloured feathers in their hackles, and brassy feathers on wings, whilst the hens were several shades lighter.

In shape the Pekin Bantam should be a miniature Cochin fowl, and should conform to the following description :—Head, small ; beak, short and nicely curved ; comb, single and very small, perfectly upright, and even in serrations ; wattles, fair length, nicely rounded ; neck, short and covered with abundant hackles ; body, deep, wide, short, and well rounded, free from angularity. Short back, full cushion, small wings carried well up ; tail, short and soft ; legs should be short in thighs and shanks, and the latter profusely covered with feathers, right to the end of the middle and outer toes ; weights, cock, 32-oz. or under, hen 28-oz. or under ; beak, legs and feet should be yellow ; face, comb, lobes and wattles should be red.

When selecting stock for breeding care should be taken to select short square blocky looking birds, as wide in front as at the back, very low on leg, very soft in tail and hock feathers, and with well-feathered toes.

104

THE BUFFS

Taking the Buffs as the leading colour, they should be one level shade of buff from head to tail, a golden tone being preferred to one of a ruddy, or more rufous shade. To produce this shade in the chickens it is wise when breeding to breed from very level rich coloured parents without any trace of white, grey, or mealy feathers about them ; if the cock is a trifle too warm in colour, or is a bit dark in wings or tail, the fault may be accounted a good one so far as breeding is concerned, as it will counteract the tendency which all Buffs have of running light. If the cock and his mates are both above the average in colour they will breed chickens which will also be too ruddy in colour. On the other hand if both sides are inclined to be light the chickens will come far too pale for exhibition purposes, whilst some of them possibly will show white in under-colour and in flights and tail. Buffs need to be protected from the sun or the beauty of their colour will quickly depart.

THE BLACKS

Blacks, which were the second colour in Cochins to come to us from China, should be a rich glossy greenish-black, the colour going well down to the roots, and the top being covered with lustre or sheen. The legs, as in the other colours, should be yellow, but it is not insisted upon, and dusky hued ones are admitted. In breeding, the same lines may be followed as advised in the chapter on Rosecombs.

THE WHITES

Whites should be of a dead snow white colour, and in selecting birds for breeding all those showing a creamy or strawy appearance should be avoided. In some strains where the leg colour is very strongly developed the plumage is tinged with a creamy hue. The best time to select the breeding stock for Whites is when the chickens are newly hatched. Those that are white when they make their appearance are seldom a good colour later on, whilst those which are sooty and dusky-looking in their first coat generally moult out into the desired dead white. Should a strain show signs of losing its colour and becoming creamy, a black cross should be resorted to with a view to restore soundness of colour. This can be done by breeding from a black hen or pullet, and then using the pullets bred therefrom, but not any of the cockerels for at least two generations, if not three.

White chickens need plenty of shade, or they will become sunburnt or " weathered " and thus be useless for exhibition. This point should be remembered in connection with the selection of breeding stock. A bird should not be rejected on the ground of unsound colour if the unsoundness is the result of exposure to the weather.

White Pekins are essentially a breed for country fanciers, and very handsome indeed do they look strutting across a closely cropped lawn.

THE CUCKOOS

The colour of Cuckoo Pekins should be a pale blue-grey ground crossed with markings of a darker blue slate colour. These markings should be of a blurred character and merge distinctly into the ground colour, thus producing the appearance generally known as Cuckoo, and differing from the clear, sharp and distinct barring seen in such varieties as the Plymouth Rock. At the present time a good strain of Cuckoo Pekin Bantams could be relied upon to reproduce good specimens for a considerable period without any out-cross. Experience will teach the breeder when it may become necessary to re-introduce Black blood. In breeding Cuckoo Pekins never use a cock that shows white in wings or tail. The cock at all times should be thoroughly sound in colour and marking ; with the hens a little more latitude may be allowed, and a little weakness in marking or of colour in wings or tail overlooked. If, however, these faults are allowed in the cock they are almost certain to reproduce in his progeny, hence the need for only sound coloured cocks being used in the breeding pen. Another thing to avoid is incorrect markings. Discard birds which are too broad or coarse in markings, also those which are too sharp and distinct and those which are broken and irregular.

THE PARTRIDGE

Partridge Pekins were the result of crossing Buffs and Blacks, and small specimens of the Large Cochins. The Partridge Pekin Bantam should resemble the Partridge Cochin in all points except size, and should answer to the following description :—Cock : neck and saddle hackle, orange red, striped with black ; back and wing bows, rich crimson ; breast, legs, foot feather, wing bar and tail, glossy green-black ; wing end (when closed), a bright bay ; the flights are black on the inner side of the web. Hen : neck hackle, golden yellow with some black striping ; body and wings and other plumage, pale brown with a golden tinge, each feather finely marked round with rich greenish-black ; tail feathers, black, except top two, which should match body colour.

The rules to be observed in breeding Partridge Pekins are those which govern the production of Partridge Wyandotte Bantams, and the faults to be guarded against are the same ; therefore I refer my readers to my notes in the chapter on Wyandottes.

THE SPANGLES

Our English Pekins are very pretty, charmingly so, but they none of them can compare with the lovely little Spangle Pekins which are bred on the Continent, and which I have seen in Belgium and Holland.

Other English fanciers who have seen them have been quite as hardly smitten by their charms as myself. The Spangles or Millifleurs are tri-coloured like unto our own English Game Bantams. In shape and feathering they are not the equal of our English Cochins, but this could easily be remedied, and if some enterprising fancier would import a few pairs and perfect them in the points mentioned, I feel sure he would be well repaid. The Mottles are black with white mottling.

FOOT FEATHERING

One of the greatest difficulties experienced by lovers of Pekins is the keeping of the foot feather in proper condition for showing, and various are the expedients resorted to to prevent damage to this important property. Some recommend six inches deep of dry river or sea sand, or peat moss litter in their runs. Others advocate having the birds out on finely shaven lawns, but in either case they will scratch, and in scratching, harm comes to the feathers of the feet. One of our most successful exhibitors was the late Mr. Binns, and his method of keeping the best exhibition birds was to have them up always in the usual exhibition pens. He had a large wooden structure fitted up like a small show-room, and here were exhibition Pekin and Booted Bantams week in and week out, and month in and month out, except when they were at the shows. About moulting or breeding time he had them out on grass runs, but all idea of exhibiting such birds was for the time given up. The cages were brushed out regularly once every day, if not twice, and the bottoms strewn with fine sand, thus keeping everything clean and sweet. When birds are mated up for breeding their foot feather should be clipped, also the fluff round the vent. If this is done the percentage of fertile eggs will be considerably higher than if it is neglected. The hens are most excellent sitters and splendid mothers, looking well after their chicks.

Pekin Bantams are very contented ; the smallest run will usually suffice owing to their docility and tameness. A very low wire-netting fence will keep them safely within bounds, and even when they have their liberty they seldom stray far away from home. Therefore they make most excellent pets for fanciers with limited accommodation. Their advantages over the clean-legged varieties are that they do not scratch half so much in a garden, where they really are splendid scavengers. They are more contented in a small space and do not require the exercise necessary to the more sprightly breeds ; and as to flying over a wall or hedge, or getting into a neighbour's premises, I should say they have never been known to do such a thing. Their docility has, however, one drawback—they are inclined to become fat and lazy. This being so, great care must be taken in feeding them. They should be fed sparingly, and maize, hemp and other fattening foods should never be given them, but green food should be given them liberally.

The perches given to Pekins should be very broad, and only raised some eight or nine inches off the floor, so as to prevent the birds breaking their foot feathers when flying down.

CHAPTER XIX

BRAHMAS, BOOTED, PLYMOUTH ROCKS, SCOTS GREYS, ANCONAS, HAMBURGHS, SUSSEX, BARNEVELDERS

BRAHMAS

IT is strange, but Brahma Bantams do not meet with the same measure of approbation as do their close cousins the Pekins. They should resemble the large Brahma Fowls in shape, carriage, colour and feather. The general treatment and feeding should be similar to that mentioned in the chapter for Pekins. So far as colour production is concerned the same system of breeding the darks should be followed as is recommended in the notes on Silver Pencilled Wyandottes, whilst those given on the Columbian Wyandottes will apply to the lights.

For some reason or other the Brahma Bantam, beautiful as it is, has not taken the fancy of Bantam breeders to any great extent. It has never been one of the popular breeds. Why, it is difficult to say. At the present moment there is a big opening for any enterprising breeder who would take the variety up and push it hard and strongly to the front.

BOOTED

These seem to almost have died out. One seldom sees a Booted Bantam at our shows in these days ; yet they have a beauty and a quaintness all their own. In shape they are taller and slimmer than the Cochins, and have a more sprightly, upright carriage than either the Brahmas or the Pekins. The general treatment and breeding arrangements given for the Pekins are equally suitable for the Booted. Booted Bantams are quite as pretty and quaint as the other feather-legged varieties, and it seems strange they should have almost disappeared.

Years ago I have seen classes of over a dozen Booteds in the several colours, whites, blacks, and mottles. In addition, one often used to see the Whiskered variety, which differed from the other in the fact that there were little tufts of feather on the sides of the face ; these were known as whiskers, or muffs, and from them came the name of the variety.

On the Continent one still sees Black, White, Spangled, and Porcelaine Booted Bantams, in Holland, particularly, the Booted is a great favourite.

PLYMOUTH ROCKS

These are amongst the varieties which have shown an upward movement in recent years. It is many years since Barred Rock Bantams appeared, and for a time it looked as though they would become very popular, but the boom did not last. During the present decade, however, they have again found friends, and not only have the Barred taken a new lease of life, but some most excellent Whites and Buffs have been shown. Type is the great essential in Rock Bantams, and that is where many of those seen have failed. The Beautiful grey colour and barring of the Plymouth Rock fowl has been well reproduced, the quality of feather has been good, as have head points and leg colour. The conditions covering the colour production are similar to those in Cuckoo Pekins, but it must ever be remembered that the Plymouth Rock colour is not black and white, but two shades of grey—a dark steel, and a light grey. The Whites and Buffs may be bred upon the same lines as those advocated for these colours in the chapter on Wyandottes.

SCOTS GREYS

These are very pretty, and are more largely kept in the land of their origin than in England. The ground colour is a light steel grey, with rich green-black barring.

The call is now for this barring to be distinct, but years ago it was otherwise. Olden time breeders used to like the barring and ground to merge, and give a sort of blurred effect. This was due, possibly, to a desire to keep Scots Greys distinct from Plymouth Rocks. Nowadays the barring must be crisp, clear and even. The face comb, lobes and wattles must all be bright red. The legs should be very fine in bone, white in colour, and quite free from feathers. The Scotties are smart, alert, sprightly little members of the Bantam family, and year by year their followers are becoming more numerous.

In breeding, type and carriage must be kept well to the front so as to avoid any resemblance to the Plymouth Rock, the Scots Grey being much more lively and alert than the Rock. In other respects the same line of breeding and management may be followed.

ANCONAS

Thus far not many Ancona Bantams have been seen, but they are a decided acquisition to the family, and should not be difficult to breed. Type and colour are the chief points to aim at, but it must never be forgotten that the mottled leg adds greatly to their charm. An Ancona Bantam rich in sheen and depth of colour, nicely mottled all over and possessing a rich red face, comb, and wattles, with ivory-like lobes, is indeed a handsome little bird.

HAMBURGHS

The Hamburghs are quite a modern production, and very handsome they are, possessing as they do the wonderful colouring and marking of the Silver and Golden Spangled and Pencilled Hamburgh Fowls. The Silver Spangled seems to be the most extensively bred thus far, but breeders have much difficulty in the task of securing smallness of body and keeping the spangles or moons from merging.

LIGHT SUSSEX

In 1920, Light Sussex Bantams made their first appearance in the show pen, and immediately were received with favour, and many congratulations paid to Mr. F. W. Smalley, their originator. For three years previous, Mr. Smalley had been working upon them, and had achieved a great triumph. They differ only from the Columbian Wyandotte in that they have a single comb, and white legs and feet, and in shape they have the long deep body of the Sussex Fowl, as opposed to the shorter and more cobby form of the Wyandotte. With these exceptions the description I have given of the Columbian Wyandotte may be applied to the Light Sussex. The rules governing the selection of breeding stock are practically the same. They are a beautiful addition to our breeds of Bantams.

A few Speckled also Red Sussex Bantams have been seen in the last few years, but neither in type, colour, nor size do they equal the Lights, and breeders have a long way to go yet before these two varieties may be said to be fixed.

THE BARNEVELDER

In 1928 Barnevelder Bantams were introduced, but as they are yet in the making not much can be said about them. Thus far the few that have been seen have shown great diversity in type, colour, and marking. When perfected the Laced Barnevelder Bantam should be a notable addition to present-day breeds.

CHAPTER XX

THE RHODE ISLAND RED

TWENTY years ago, when the big Rhode Island Red was just making a name for itself in this country, a well-known authority wrote: " This is an American breed which need not detain us long. It has no merit as an exhibition fowl." There must have been prejudice behind the statement, because even then the Red was popular, and has since become the most popular of exhibition birds in this country. A few years back several fanciers set themselves the task of Bantamising the Rhode Island Red, but the most perfervid could not assert that they have been successful. Why it is hard to say.

We have had birds of the desired colour, and others of the desired shape, but thus far we are a long way from the ideal. The birds that have approached the desired character have been too gamey in type, and have not had the correct Rhode Island Red carriage, whilst those which have had good type have been too big, and not deep enough in colour.

A SUGGESTION FOR MATING

In their endeavours to produce this variety fanciers have used the following Bantams: Old English Game, Modern Game and Partridge Wyandottes, and possibly others, but thus far without meeting with the result they desired. This applies not only to the efforts of English breeders, but to those of America as well.

Possibly if a small late-bred Rhode Island Red cockerel was used with some of the Rhode Island Red Bantam hens now in existence, an improvement would be made so far as colour is concerned. The shape and size would possibly be improved by taking a trio of late-bred Rhode Island Red pullets and mating them to a small good-coloured Rhode Island Red Bantam cockerel. Then, by selecting the smallest from each of such matings, paying due regard to colour, success might be attained in a couple or three seasons.

The standard colour and shape of the Rhode Island Red is so steadfast and so well known that I need not say more here than that all one has to do is to Bantamise it. The field is a very open one. The outstanding bird has not yet been produced, and a careful, thoughtful breeder starting now could easily in two or three seasons be farther on the road than any of the present-day breeders of Rhode Island Red Bantams. It is strange that further progress has not been made.

CHAPTER XXI

FRIZZLES

DURING the last ten years these lovely little birds have made a bit of a move, and have been taken up by several new fanciers. This has been most pleasing to me, the oldest fancier of the variety in England. Why the Frizzles have not enjoyed greater popularity in the past I cannot understand. They are quite as hardy as many of the more popular breeds ; they are very handsome little creatures ; whilst for those who like something quaint and out of the common they have many charms. My first connection with Frizzles goes back over forty-five years.

When I first commenced breeding Frizzles there was no standard to breed to, and no one knew whether they should be rose-combed or single-combed ; both used to win. Some had white legs, some willow, some mottled, some blue, and some pale yellow, but not the rich yellow which is now expected and generally seen, and which I introduced. As I have said, combs were not by any means a decided quantity, quite as many birds coming with rose as with single combs. The single comb is much the best, in my opinion, combining and being more in harmony with the peculiar feathering of the Frizzle, in the same manner as does the rich yellow leg. To-day one never sees a rose-combed Frizzle.

SPLENDID BROODIES

The Frizzles are very tame and docile, make splendid " broodies," and most excellent mothers. One well-known writer has said that whilst " the curled hens are excellent mothers and sitters, the plain feathered ones are not to be depended on in either capacity. This seems strange, but nevertheless it is quite true." One does not like to dispute so decided a statement from a recognised Bantam authority, yet I must dispute this. I have used the plain feathered birds over and over again, and they are most excellent mothers. Why should they be otherwise?

April and May are the best months in which to hatch Frizzles, later hatched ones seldom do well. The late autumn months are not conducive to a successful moult.

BREEDING PLAIN FEATHER BIRDS

Most breeders of Frizzles run four hens with a cock, and sometimes two of the four will be plain or smooth feathered, that is, birds without curl. Sometimes all the hens will be plain feathered, but very rarely will they all be frizzled. If the cock is plain feathered, then the hens used are generally all frizzled, although some make a regular practice of having both plain and frizzled hens in the pen, be the cock either plain feathered or frizzled. The reason for this is because if all the birds are frizzled the feather, especially of the cocks, is apt to get too fine and narrow, in a word, too "silkified." What is wanted is nice broad feather, with plenty of strength, not only in the fibre, but also in the stem of the feather.

Another point upon which judges go wrong is shape. The standard says the back should be broad and the chest round. Yet lately I have seen birds winning which were very narrow in back, and pointed in chest. A broad back and chest are needed so as to show the curl.

Owing to so much White and Black Rosecomb blood having been introduced into the Frizzles, many birds come with wrong coloured lobes and legs. Yellow legs and red lobes are required, but every now and then a real good bird turns up so far as shape, carriage and curl are concerned, which is lacking in these essentials, but possesses beautiful white lobes and legs. Such birds should be killed, because these points are very difficult to breed out, and if you breed with birds possessing them, how is it possible to preserve the desired red lobes and yellow legs? Crossing with the Japanese has given birds that are too short in legs, and have the shuffling carriage of the Japanese, and a too low carriage of the wings. The carriage of the Frizzle should be smart and alert.

Frizzles require great care to be exercised in preparing for the show bench, far more than is needed with ordinary plain feathered birds. The washing process, of course, is the same in each case, but not so the drying. With plain feathered birds the tail has to be kept to the fire to bring the feather down into its place. Thus there is little fear of the face being scorched. But with Frizzles the feather is wanted the other way up. Therefore, as much as possible the face must be turned towards the fire, and the tail away from it. This needs constant watchfulness whilst the birds are drying, otherwise the face, wattles, and comb will suffer. A slow fire is best for the purpose, as a fast, fierce one will soon do more harm than good.

THE END

Printed in the United Kingdom by
Lightning Source UK Ltd., Milton Keynes
142118UK00001B/25/A